# Imaginative writing

KEY STAGE
TWO

PHOTOCOPIABLES

*impact*

WRITING HOMEWORK

Published by Scholastic Ltd,
Villiers House,
Clarendon Avenue,
Leamington Spa,
Warwickshire CV32 5PR

UNIVERSITY OF
NORTH LONDON

Activities by the IMPACT Project at the
University of North London, collated
and rewritten by Ruth Merttens,
Alan Newland and Susie Webb

**Editor** Gill Munton
**Assistant editors** Ben Orme & Jane Bishop
**Designer** Louise Belcher
**Series designer** Anna Oliwa
**Illustrations** Amanda Wood & James Alexander
**Cover illustration** Headlines, Charlbury, Oxford

Designed using Aldus Pagemaker
Printed in Great Britain by Clays Ltd,
Bungay, Suffolk

**British Library Cataloguing-in-Publication Data**
A catalogue record for this book is
available from the British Library.

ISBN 0-590-53372-X

impact
WRITING HOMEWORK

# KEY STAGE TWO

## CONTENTS

*impact*
WRITING HOMEWORK

# impact
## INTRODUCTION

IMPACT books are designed to help teachers involve parents in children's learning to write. Through the use of interesting and specially developed writing tasks, parents can encourage and support their child's efforts as they become confident and competent writers.

The shared writing programme is modelled on the same process as the IMPACT shared maths which encompasses a non-traditional approach to homework.

This is outlined in the following diagram:

> The teacher selects a task based on the work she is doing in class. The activity may relate to the children's work in a particular topic, to the type of writing they are engaged in or to their reading.

> The teacher prepares the children for what they have to do at home. This may involve reading a particular story, playing a game or having a discussion with the children about the task.

> The children take home the activity, and share it with someone at home. This may be an older brother/sister, a parent or grandparent or any other friend or relation.

> The parents and children respond to the activity by commenting in an accompanying diary or notebook.
> \* This mechanism provides the teacher with valuable feedback.

> The teacher uses what was done at home as the basis for follow-up work in class. This may involve further writing, drawing, reading or discussion.

The activities in this book have been designed to enable children to develop and expand their writing skills in conversation with those at home. Where possible the activities reflect the context of the home rather than the school, and draw upon experiences and events from out-of-school situations.

## Shared activities – or homework with chatter!

Importantly, the activities are designed to be shared. Unlike traditional homework, where the child is expected to 'do it alone' and not to have help, with IMPACT they are encouraged – even required – to find someone to talk to and share the activity with. With each task we say the following should be true:
- something is said;
- something is written;
- something is read.

Sometimes the main point of the IMPACT activity is the discussion – and so we do try to encourage parents to see that the task involves a lot more than just completing a piece of writing. It is very important that teachers go through the task carefully with the children so that they know what to do. Clearly not all the children, or parents, will be able to read the instructions in English and so this preparation is crucial if the children are

to be able to share the activity. The sheet often acts more as a backup or a prompt than a recipe.

## Diaries

The shared writing works by involving parents in their children's learning. The IMPACT diaries\* are a crucial part of this process. They provide a mechanism by means of which an efficient parent-teacher-dialogue is established. These diaries enable teachers to obtain valuable feedback both about children's performances in relation to specific activities and about the tasks themselves. Parents are able to alert the teacher to any matter of concern or pleasant occurrences, and nothing is left to come as a big surprise or a horrible shock in the end of year report. It is difficult to exaggerate the importance of the IMPACT diaries. The OFSTED inspectors and HMI have highly commended their effectiveness in helping to raise children's achievements and in developing a real partnership with parents.
\* See the Afterword (page 128) for details of where to obtain these.

## Timing

Most schools send the Shared Writing activities fortnightly. Many interleave these activities with the IMPACT maths tasks, thus ensuring that the children have something to share with their parents almost every week. Many schools also use the shared writing tasks to enhance their shared reading or PACT programme. It has been found that some parents may be encouraged to take a renewed interest in reading a book with their child on a regular basis when the shared writing project is launched in a class. However, there are a variety of practices and the important point is that each teacher should feel comfortable with how often IMPACT is sent in her class.

## Parent friendly

It is important for the success of the IMPACT Shared Writing that parents are aware of both the purpose and the extent of each activity. Many teachers adopt a developmental approach to writing, encouraging emergent writing or the use of invented spellings. Care has to be taken to share the philosophy behind this approach with parents, and to select activities which will not assume that parents are as familiar with the implications as teachers. You will get lots of support if parents can see that what they are doing is helping their child to become cheerful and successful writers!

To facilitate this process, each activity contains a note to parents which helps to make it clear what the purpose of the activity is, and how they can best help. The activities also contain hints to help parents share the activity in an enjoyable and effective manner. Sometimes the hints contain ideas, or starting points. On other occasions they may be examples or demonstrations of how to set about the task concerned.

It is always important to bear in mind that parents can, and sometimes should, do things differently at home. At home, many children will enjoy, and even benefit from, copying underneath a line of text or writing without paying attention to spelling or punctuation, where in school such things might not be expected or encouraged. The most successful partnerships between home and school recognise both the differences and the similarities in each other's endeavours.

## Planning

The shared writing activities are divided into three sections according to age: Reception, Year 1 and Year 2. There are two pages of teachers' notes relating to the individual activities at the beginning of each section. When selecting which activity to send home with the children it is helpful to remember the following:

- Ideally, we send the same activity with each child in the class or year. The activities are mostly designed to be as open-ended as possible, to allow for a wide variety of different levels of response. Teachers often add a few extra comments of their own to a particular sheet to fit it to the needs of a particular child or group of children with special educational needs. It is also important to stress that the child does not have to do all the actual writing – often the parent does half or more. The point of the activity may lie in the discussion and the creation of a joint product.
- It is useful to send a variety of different activities. Some children will particularly enjoy a word game, while others will prefer a task which includes drawing a picture. Activities may be used to launch a topic, to support a particular project, to enable a good quality of follow-up to an idea and to revise or practise particular skills. Much of the benefit of the shared writing exercise may be derived from the follow-up work back in the classroom. Therefore, it is very important to select activities which will feed into the type of work being focused upon at that time. For example, if the class is working on grammatical categories, verbs, nouns, etc., then an activity requiring that children and parents produce real and fictional definitions of long words will fit in well. On the other hand, if the class is doing some work on fairy stories, making a **wanted** poster of a character in a story may be appropriate.

## Notes to teachers

These give suggestions to the teachers. They outline what may be done before the activity is sent to ensure that it goes well at home. And they describe how the activity may be followed up as part of routine classwork during the subsequent week. More help with what happens when the activity comes back is to be found in the Afterword on page 128.

## Parent letter and booklet

It is very important that parents are kept informed about the nature of this new-style homework. Most schools elect to launch IMPACT Shared Writing by having a meeting or a series of meetings. We have included here a draft letter to parents and a booklet which schools may photocopy and give to parents. The booklet is eight A5 pages when copied, folded and collated. This can be given to all new parents as their children start school. There is a space on the cover for the school name.

## Keeping shared writing going...

There are a few tips which have been found over the years to make life simpler for parents, teachers and children:

- Don't send shared writing activities in the first few weeks of the September term. Shared writing, like IMPACT maths, usually starts in the third week of the new school year.
- Don't send shared writing activities in the second half of the summer term. Shared writing, like IMPACT maths, usually belongs to the heart of the school year.
- Do value the work that the children and their parents do at home. Sometimes it may not be presented as you expect – for example, a lot of parents with young children write in upper case rather than lower case letters or will ask children to **write over** a line of print. Remember that what comes back into class is a starting point for work that you consider appropriate, and is facilitating both discussion and partnership.

Dear Parents,

In our class, we have decided to use a new 'shared homework scheme' designed to help develop and improve children's writing skills. This will involve sending home a regular task in the form of an A4 sheet. The sheet will outline a simple writing activity for you and your child to enjoy together. These are designed to be shared; the children are not expected to complete the tasks alone.

We would very much like to talk to you about this scheme, and so on _____ we shall hold three short meetings. You need only come to **one** of these and can choose the time which is most convenient:

- 9.00 in the morning
- 3.30 in the afternoon
- 7.00 in the evening.

We would really like as many parents as possible to attend.

Your help in supporting your child's learning is a crucial part of his/her success at school. We do appreciate the time and trouble that parents take with their children, and we can certainly see the benefits in the quality of the children's work and the enthusiasm with which they attack it.

Please return the slip at the bottom of the letter.

Yours sincerely,

_____

Name _____     Class _____

I would like to attend the meeting at:

9.00 in the morning

3.30 in the afternoon

7.00 in the evening

Please tick **one** time only.

## Don't forget...

**Pick your time!**
When you both want
to do the activity.

**Don't over-correct!**
This can be very
discouraging.

**Your child does not always
have to do all the writing!**
You may take turns, or take
over sometimes.

**Make it fun!**
If either of you gets tired
or bored help a bit more.
Tasks should not last more
than 20 minutes unless you
want them to!

**Praise and encourage as
much as you can!**

# IMPACT

## Shared Writing

SPIKe

**School name**

# About Shared Writing

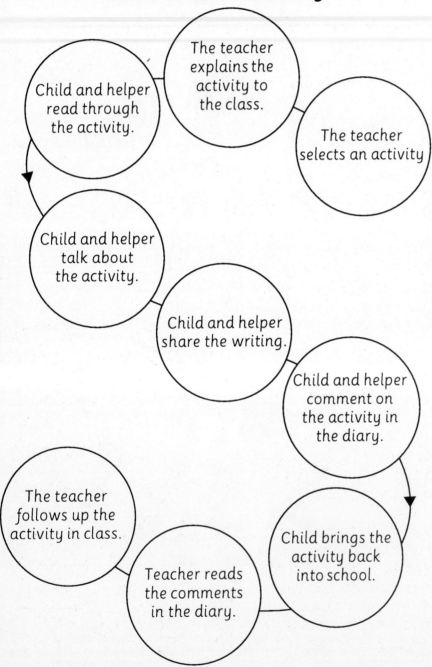

The teacher selects an activity

The teacher explains the activity to the class.

Child and helper read through the activity.

Child and helper talk about the activity.

Child and helper share the writing.

Child and helper comment on the activity in the diary.

Child brings the activity back into school.

Teacher reads the comments in the diary.

The teacher follows up the activity in class.

# Spelling and punctuation

We all agree that correct spelling and punctuation are very important. However........

## DO

- Notice punctuation when sharing the writing activity.
- Talk about different uses of capital and lower case letters.
- Play word games such as 'I spy' or 'Hangman'.
- Read what the child has written before you make any comment about spelling, punctuation or presentation.
- Help them learn any words sent home by the school.

## DON'T

- Worry about every mistake – children can become very anxious about their writing if constantly interrupted.
- With young children don't insist that they spell every word correctly. At this stage we are encouraging them to 'be writers'.
- Don't worry if your child is quite slow to learn to spell and punctuate – these things come with time and encouragement.

## How we write

Writing also has a mechanical side, children have to learn to form their letters, to separate words, to begin and end sentences.

When children are first learning to write it can be very discouraging to be constantly corrected. However, as they become more confident, we can afford to draw their attention to these things:

## Becoming independent...

As they get older children need encouragement to become independent readers and writers. But this doesn't mean that there is no role for a supportive parent. In some ways your help is more and not less necessary...

• Talk about the book they are reading – or even comics or magazines etc. This really helps to encourage children to read. Ask questions like:
What do you like about this book?
What exciting things happen? Tell me the story...
Which books are good and which are boring?

• Try to read some of the books your child reads. This really gives you a shared experience – and lots to talk about!

• Help them to become confident and independent spellers...

**Don't** shout because they spell something wrongly!
**Do** encourage them by looking for letter patterns.
**Don't** mock a child who finds spelling hard.
**Do** make a SHORT list of common words and pin it up in the bathroom where everyone sees it every day!

# Being a writer...

Is about...
Having ideas
Composing them
Communicating them

WANTED

A Purpose

a.k.a.

A Greeting
A Compliment
An Enquiry
A Gossip
A Thought.

To An Audience
my teacher
mum or Dad
Friend or Foe
Near or Far

Choose from our
catalogue of
Types of Writing

a letter
a poster
a list
a book

# Parents can help by...

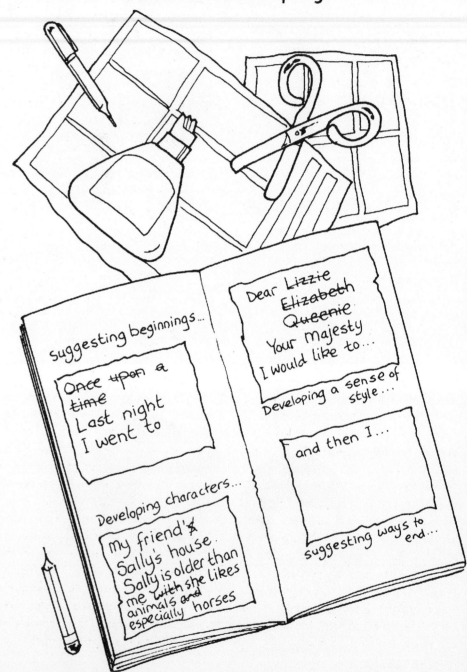

Suggesting beginnings...

Once ~~upon a time~~
Last night
I went to

Dear ~~Lizzie~~
~~Elizabeth~~
~~Queenie~~
Your majesty
I would like to...

Developing a sense of
style...

and then I...

Developing characters...

My friend's
Sally's house.
Sally is older than
me ~~with~~ she likes
animals ~~and~~
especially horses

suggesting ways to
end...

# Teachers' Notes
## YEAR THREE

**Stage names** Talk about the names that the children have chosen. How have they made them sound suitably impressive? Try writing some stories about these characters in the classroom. An extension of this might be to design the costume or the set for a particular scene.

**The things I don't like** These rhyming couplets could easily be incorporated into a class poem. This could be written out in large, clear writing and displayed on the wall for the children to read for themselves. This is only one of the many different ways of writing poetry, so make sure that the activity is not done in isolation; read a wide selection of different styles of poetry to the children, and talk about them.

**Wacky nursery rhymes** Share all the nursery rhymes, and compile them into a 'Wacky nursery rhyme' book, complete with illustrations. This could be a good introduction to nonsense poetry such as that of Edward Lear. Discuss the 'word pictures' that he is able to conjure up even though he has invented some of the words. Alternatively, the book could be used as a starting point for finding out about stories behind the nursery rhymes; where did they come from, and how old are they?

*Book of nonsense* Edward Lear (Dent).

**Space adventure** Talk about the characters, settings and plots that the children have thought of. The children could write their stories as scripts, scene by scene. A good art/design activity is to build sets for the space adventures. Give each child a large card-board box and cut away at least one of the sides and the top, leaving the back, the base and the sides for decoration. The children could make Plasticine models for characters and props.

**No more than ten words** Play the game with the whole class. Use some of the children's definitions, and see if the others can guess what they were writing about. Ask what was the hardest part of the game. The next time you are writing as a class, try 'banning' the use of a few words, and make the children suggest some alternatives before you start.

**Super cereal** Look at the logos together, and discuss what kind of cereal they might represent. Look at a selection of real cereal packets, and ask the children to write their own advertising slogans. Get them to think up some special offers or free gifts to entice new customers to try the products. Make models of the cereal packets (a realistic way to do this is to use real cereal boxes turned inside out and covered with white or coloured paper), and display them.

**Three wishes** Talk about the wishes the children suggested; was it as easy as they expected? Had they thought through the consequences of their wishes? Read some stories about wish-granting with the children, and talk about whether the characters had thought their wishes through before they

made them. Now the children have had a chance to think about the possible consequences, would they change any of their wishes?

**Fairy tale who's who** Sort the characters into categories such as good/bad, ugly/beautiful, kind/mean. Write the names on cards and put them in a bag. Now brainstorm all the places in which an adventure could happen (real-life or magical), and then think of strange or magical objects that appear in stories (such as magic lamps or keys) and write these on cards. When the children next write a story, they can take up to three character cards and then one from each of the other bags. They then try to write a story that includes all the elements they have picked out of the bags!

**Last page surprise!** Ask the children to write their own stories using their books as a starting point. Make each one into a zig-zag book: fold a strip of paper into a zig-zag, making sure that each page is big enough to write on. The books could be four to six pages long. Try to encourage the children to use surprising endings. Talk about endings of different types – sad, happy, unexpected, sudden. Use examples to illustrate these, such as *The boy who cried wolf* by Tony Ross (Anderson Press).

**Fill the gaps** Share a few of the children's examples, then play a story game. The children sit in a circle, and take it in turns to add a sentence to a story as it develops. They can continue the game in small groups. Limit them to a certain number of turns each in which to finish the

story. If you can, place an adult or older child with each group so that they can transcribe the story as it unfolds. Once it has been written down, it can be presented in the form of a big book illustrated by the children. The group can then read it to the rest of the class at story time.

**Cartoon characters** Before this activity goes home, talk to the children about speech and thought bubbles. Afterwards, ask the children to write whole stories featuring the things characters say and the things they think.

**Consequences** After sharing a few of the children's examples, play a story game. Sit the children in a circle, and ask them to take it in turns to add a sentence to a story as it develops. They can continue the game in small groups. Limit them to a certain number of turns each in which to finish the story. If you can, place an adult or older child with each group so that they can transcribe the story as it unfolds. Once it has been written down, it can be presented in the form of a big book illustrated by the children. The group can then read it to the rest of the class at story time.

**Nasty names** Collect all the names and make a list. Sort the names; are they sneaky, violent, powerful, stupid, mean? Ask the children to choose names they particularly like and write descriptions of those characters; what they look like, where they live, what they do on a daily basis. Try to think up some 'good' character names that could be incorporated into the stories about the nasty characters. Use the children's storylines in subsequent drama sessions in small groups.

**What ending?** Endings can be happy or sad, open or closed. They can be predictable or unexpected, sudden or slow. What sort of endings do the children prefer? Finally, read the end of a book and ask them to write down what happens before that. (You will need to choose a book which none of them know.) Then read them the actual story!

**Ouch!** The anecdotes could be used in drama work, where the children are given the opportunity to mime their terrible accidents to the others, or it could be used as a starting point for written work. Pairs of children take turns to be a newspaper reporter and the subject of the accident. The reporter must take notes (writing or pictures – anything that will help them remember.) If you have the facilities, the reporters could dictate their notes to a 'secretary' (adult) who can type up the article on the computer. It could then be developed into a kind of newspaper. If a typist is not available, the children can write up their own notes.

**Strange foods** Put all the lists together; are there any foods which surprised the children? Talk about how diet has changed over time, and how what we eat is far more influenced by international cuisine than it was sixty years ago. Discuss how diet may change in the next twenty years; consider vegetarianism, climate changes, food prices, hi-tech kitchen equipment, conservation, healthier eating and convenience foods.

**Design a wrapper** Talk about the product names the children have thought of, and sort them into categories (citrus fruit, tropical fruit, new flavours, chocolate). Make the designs into 3D models – use pieces of card that can be rolled into the shape of a cone, or turn inside out a small flat box, cover it with white paper and stick a lolly stick into the base. Look at a few real wrappers to help the children remember the information they carry. Staple or pin these models on the wall!

**Space dragons** Read out a few of the children's examples, and try to build up a story about an encounter between the child and the space dragon. The classroom could be converted into a space dragon cave or spaceship, with space dragons made out of junk materials looming from every corner.

**Scary dreams** Ask a few children to retell their scary dreams, if they do not mind doing this. They could write their dreams as a sequence of events in the form of a cartoon strip. Can the children invent some dream characters, such as enormous cats or tiny hand-sized elephants? They could then draw the creatures and write descriptions.

**Up a gum tree** These three sentences will give the children a starting point for writing more extended stories. Children could write out their stories as narratives or turn them into cartoons.

**In a hole** These three sentences will give the children a starting point for writing more extended stories. They could write their stories on round pieces of paper, to be collated into a 'round' class book complete with illustrations.

**Rainy again** These short rhymes could be written out in large colourful letters as part of a wall display. Each rhyme could be framed by a giant raindrop. You could also use the rhymes as part of a music/ drama session where the children put their words to a repeating rhyme using percussion instruments. They could add a sentence of dance movements.

**Yummy scrummy** Before you send this activity home, read the poem 'Chocolate cake' by Michael Rosen. Rosen describes the cake in an evocative way which may help the children with their own descriptions. Compile the children's rhymes into a class book of food poems. (You may want to put a warning on them: 'Not to be read just before a meal!')
*Quick, let's get out of here!* Michael Rosen (Puffin Books)

**'Don't put fat on the cat...'** Before you send this activity home, read the poem 'Don't put mustard in the custard' by Michael Rosen from his book of the same title. When the children bring back their rhymes, compile them into a class book of 'don't poems. For a contrast, some children could write 'do' poems.
*Don't put mustard in the custard* Michael Rosen (Andre Deutsch)

**Animal errors** Ask the children to hold up their illustrations and retell their stories. (You could spread these out over the day, or have a few children tell their stories at each storytime.) Read some funny animal stories with the children, for example *Mog, the forgetful cat.*
*Mog, The forgetful cat* Judith Kerr (Collins)

**A treasure map** Display all the children's maps, and ask a few of them what their treasure was. Who chose the most unusual treasure? Write full-length stories telling the story of the treasure – you may even want the children to tell the story from the treasure's point of view! Who did the treasure originally belong to, and why was it buried?

**The Wizard of Oz** Try to arrange a showing of the film 'The Wizard of Oz'. The film starts in black and white, and then changes to colour as soon as Dorothy lands in Oz. The children could paint pictures telling the story of the film, making sure that their pictures of Dorothy in Kansas are all in black and white. An extension of this would be to write full-length stories about what would happen if the children's own homes were damaged by a hurricane.

**Dress up** It would be fun to have a real fancy dress party once the children have planned their costumes. You could make the masks for the characters at school and then ask the children to bring what they can from home. (Children who cannot find anything at home can always have a rummage in the dressing up box!) Plan the whole party: writing invitations (perhaps to helpers in your class and younger members of the children's families), buying, cooking and preparing the food, and setting up the room.

## Stage names

- Imagine that you are a famous pop star!

- What name would you choose for your stage name?

- Draw a 'photo' of yourself for the newspaper, and write a couple of lines to go under it.

**To the helper:**

- You may need to explain what a 'stage name' is, and why people in the public eye sometimes change their names.

**Characterisation is an important aspect of creative writing, and creating a character's name helps to develop personality. Back at school, we shall collect the names the children have invented and flesh out their characters so that we can feature them in our stories or plays.**

_____and

*child*

_____

*helper(s)*

_____

did this activity together

_____and

*child*

_____

*helper(s)*

_____

did this activity together

# The things I don't like

● Write a poem in rhyming couplets about some of the things you don't like. Each pair of lines must rhyme, for example:

'Wet playtimes and semolina pudding,
I really can't stand it when my sister starts singing.'

● These two lines end with an '**-ing**' sound; the next two lines could end with a different sound. Ask your helper to help you to write the poem down on a piece of paper.

# Wacky nursery rhymes

More than a hundred years ago a writer called Lewis Carroll rewrote a children's song called 'Twinkle, twinkle little star' as part of his famous book **Alice in Wonderland**, so that it became:

'Twinkle, twinkle little bat!
How I wonder what you're at!
Up above the world you fly,
Like a tea-tray in the sky.'

● Have a go at rewriting a nursery rhyme or a favourite song in this way.

● Write your new rhyme on a piece of paper and draw a picture.

● Tell your rhyme to someone other than your helper; can he or she say the original version?

● Can your helper write one, too?

**To the helper:**

● You could rewrite a nursery rhyme and tell the new version to your child – can he or she guess the original version?

**Nursery rhymes are an important part of the children's heritage, and we shall be discussing all the different versions in the classroom. Poetry is one of a range of stimuli for writing that we try to promote in school, and similarly, children are encouraged to express themselves in a variety of forms of writing including poetry, plays, instructions and reports.**

_____and

*child*

_____

*helper(s)*

_____

did this activity together

_____and

*child*

_____

*helper(s)*

_____

did this activity together

# Space adventure

Imagine that you are going to make a film!

It is going to be a space adventure.

● On a piece of paper, write down the names of three characters you will have in your film.

● Write a description of the setting.

● Draw a picture.

● Tell your helper what is going to happen in your film.

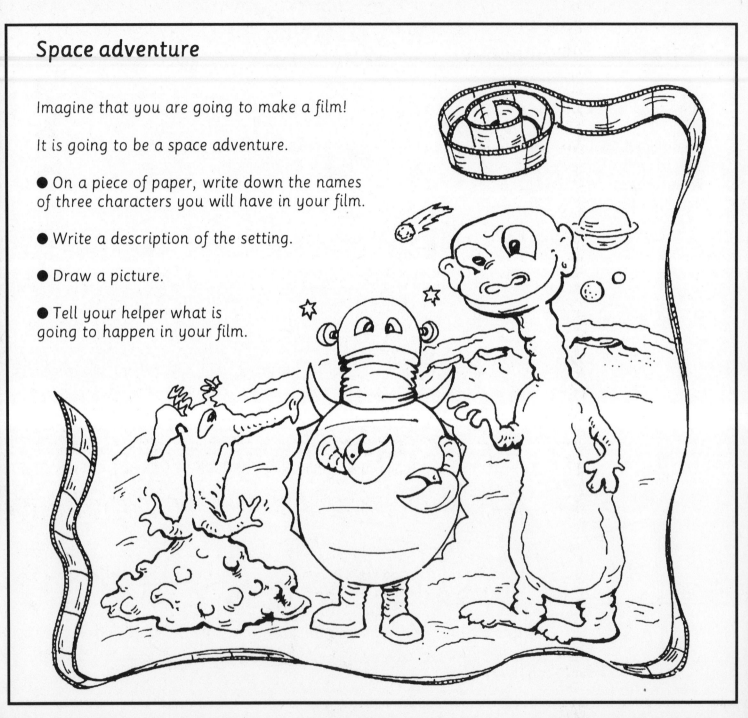

# No hesitations

● Think of an object.

● Ask your helper to write a description of it in no more than 10 words.

For example:
'Aeroplane'
'Flying people – carrier with engines and wings'

● Take it in turns to suggest objects.

**To the helper:**

● This is more difficult than it looks! Try playing the game a few times without the limitation of ten words or fewer, just to get the hang of it. Give a hand with the writing if necessary.

**This game makes the children use descriptive words and phrases which they might not usually choose to use in their spoken or written work.**

_____and

*child*

_____

*helper(s)*

_____

did this activity together

_____and

*child*

_____

*helper(s)*

_____

did this activity together

# Super cereal

Congratulations!

You have just invented the most interesting and tasty cereal ever!

● What are you going to call it?

● Can you design a logo for it?

A logo is a drawing or a piece of type that a company uses on all its products.

● Which words are you going to use on the packet to describe your cereal so that people will want to buy it?

Use any cereal packet you have at home to help you with this. Write your ideas here.

*impact* WRITING HOMEWORK

# Three wishes

- If you had three wishes, what would you wish for?

- Write down your wishes below.

(You can't wish for more wishes!)

- Can you think of any stories about three wishes?

_____and

*child*

_____

*helper(s)*

_____

did this activity together

_____and

*child*

_____

*helper(s)*

_____

did this activity together

# Fairy tale who's who

● Write a list of fairy tale characters on a piece of paper.

● Make the list as long as you can. Try to include both good and bad characters.

● Sort your list so that the characters are in different groups, for example, 'female, good'; 'female, bad'.

# Last page surprise!

● Are you reading a book at the moment?

If so, stop reading just before the last page.

● What do you think is going to happen?

● Is it obvious?

● Write your own last page for the book.

● Now look at the author's version of the last page. Which ending do you like better?

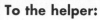

_____and

*child*

_____

*helper(s)*

_____

did this activity together

# Fill the gaps

● Work with your helper to fill in the blanks in this story and finish it off.

If you want to, you can put unexpected things in the blanks!

Once upon a time there lived a

_____

One day a prince came riding by on a

_____

He _____

_____

_____

# Cartoon characters

- Pick a part of the story in your book from school in which someone is speaking to the main character. Draw a picture below showing these two people talking.

- Show what they are saying in speech bubbles, and use thought bubbles to show what they are thinking.

**To the helper:**

- Talk about the whole story, or the part you have read so far, with your child. Discuss the different characters, and choose an interesting one to be talking to the main character. Talk about the things that they say, and how they might differ from the things they might be thinking.
- Help with the writing if necessary.

**This activity will focus your child's attention on character development and motivation.**

_____and

*child*

_____

*helper(s)*

_____

did this activity together

_____and

*child*

_____

*helper(s)*

_____

did this activity together

# Consequences

This is a game that is sometimes played at parties.

**1.** Write the name of a man or a boy at the top of a piece of paper. Fold the paper back to hide what you've written. Your helper does the same. Now swap your papers.

**2.** Write the name of a woman or a girl at the top of the new piece of paper. Fold the paper back. Your helper does the same. Now swap your papers.

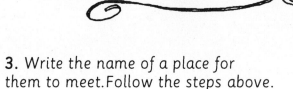

**3.** Write the name of a place for them to meet. Follow the steps above.

**4.** Write what he said to her. Follow the steps above.

**5.** Write what she said to him. Follow the steps above.

**6.** Write the consequence (what happened).

**7.** Now unfold the papers and read the stories.

# Nasty names

● Think of imaginative names for some really nasty characters in a story – make them as original as possible!

● Write down the best five here.

**To the helper:**

● Talk with your child about stories you have heard or read with really nasty characters in them, for example Cruella De Vil from *101 Dalmatians*. This will spark off ideas for new names. Maybe some other people in the house can give you a hand.

**Characterisation is an important aspect of creative writing, and helps to develop personality. Back at school, we shall collect the names the children have invented and flesh out their characters so that we can feature them in our stories or plays.**

_____and

*child*

_____

*helper(s)*

_____

did this activity together

_____and

*child*

_____

*helper(s)*

_____

did this activity together

# What ending?

● Can you remember the last book you read?

● What happened at the end?

● Did the ending explain exactly what happened, or were you left to figure it out for yourself?

● On a piece of paper, write in your own words what happened on the last page of the book.

# Ouch!

● Can you remember the worst **fall or accident** you have had?

● Draw a cartoon showing what happened, and write about it.

**To the helper:**

● Talk about your child's memories of the accident. Perhaps you can think of an accident that you had when you were a child?

● Try sharing the task; you could both do some drawing and some of the writing.

**Personal anecdotes develop children's storytelling skills. Anecdotes have a particular style and pattern depending on the teller and the listener. This activity helps children to sequence a narrative and to report on factual events.**

_____and

*child*

_____

*helper(s)*

_____

did this activity together

_____and

*child*

_____

*helper(s)*

_____

did this activity together

# Strange foods

● Think of some **foods** that your great-great-grandfather would not recognise if he came for tea, for example, a hamburger, or popcorn.

● Take turns with your helper to write the name of a food in the space opposite until you have a list.

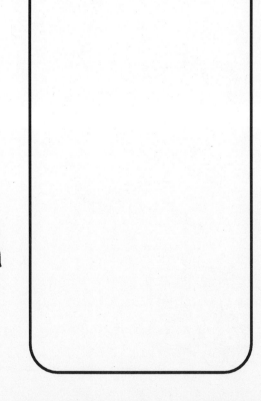

# Design a wrapper

● Design a wrapper for a new ice cream or lolly.

● What will its name be?

● What different flavours will be available?

● Draw a picture of the wrapper here. Show the name, the slogan, the price and a brief description.

**To the helper:**

● You may want to look at used wrappers or other packaging materials to help with ideas.
● Talk about favourite flavours; which would sell best in your house?

**Product name and design can be very important in determining how successful a product is. This activity draws on the child's creative abilities with the overall purpose of constructing persuasive writing.**

_____and

*child*

_____

*helper(s)*

_____

did this activity together

_____and

*child*

_____

*helper(s)*

_____

did this activity together

# Space dragons

● Imagine that a dragon arrives from outer space! What do you think it would look like? (For example, it might have rockets instead of wings! It might be wearing a space helmet!)

● Draw a picture and write a sentence about your dragon.

# Scary dreams

● Have you ever had a scary dream? Draw a picture below to show what happened. Write a few lines about it.

**To the helper:**

● Does your child ever wake up in the night with bad dreams? Talk about them; what is scary about them?

● Give a hand with the writing if necessary.

**Remembering a dream can bring back all sorts of scary images. When the children are writing their own stories they will need to be able to draw on their experiences to create believable characters and plots.**

_____and

*child*

_____

*helper(s)*

_____

did this activity together

# Up a gum tree

You are stuck in a tree!

● Write three sentences: one describing how you got there, one describing what it feels like, and one telling how you are going to be rescued!

● Draw a picture.

# In a hole

You are stuck in a hole!

● Write three sentences: one describing how you got there, one describing what it feels like, and one telling how you are going to be rescued!

● Draw a picture here.

_____and

*child*

_____

*helper(s)*

_____

did this activity together

_____and

*child*

_____

*helper(s)*

_____

did this activity together

# Rainy again!

Rain, rain, go away,
Come again another day...

● Make up your own rhyme to make the rain go away!

● Write it on a piece of paper and draw pictures to go with it.

*impact* WRITING HOMEWORK

# Yummy scrummy

'I scream, you scream,
We all scream for ice cream!'

● Can you make up a short
poem about your favourite food?

● Write it on a piece of paper and
draw your pictures to go with it.

_____and

*child*

_____

*helper(s)*

_____

did this activity together

_____and

**child**

_____

**helper(s)**

_____

did this activity together

## 'Don't put fat on the cat...'

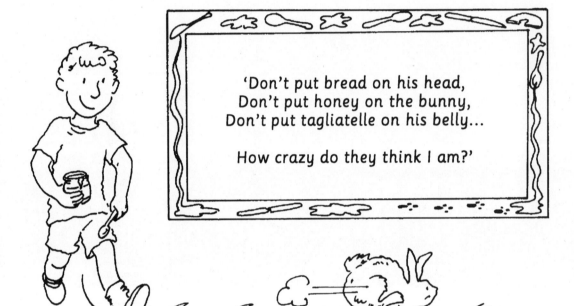

'Don't put bread on his head,
Don't put honey on the bunny,
Don't put tagliatelle on his belly...

How crazy do they think I am?'

Michael Rosen writes a poem a bit like this in his book **'Don't put mustard in the custard'**. He is making fun of some of the silly things that grown-ups say to children. Now it is your turn; can you make up at least two more silly commands? Remember to make them rhyme.

● Write them on a piece of paper and draw pictures to go with them.

*impact* WRITING HOMEWORK

# Animal errors

● Has your pet ever made a **mistake**?

For example, imagine a rather over-curious cat falling headfirst into a fish tank while watching the fish!

● Write about an 'animal error' which made you laugh. Perhaps you and your helper could take turns to write sentences.

● Write your story on a piece of paper and draw pictures to go with it.

**To the helper:**

● Talk about the pets you both know with your child.
● Always stress kindness to animals; if an animal is in distress it should be helped rather than ridiculed.

**This activity asks children to report on a factual event, paying attention to the sequence.**

_____and

*child*

_____

*helper(s)*

_____

did this activity together

_____and

*child*

_____

*helper(s)*

did this activity together

# A treasure map

● You will need a large piece of paper. Draw a map showing where some secret treasure is hidden.

● Write a few sentences about how to find the treasure.

# The Wizard of Oz

Imagine that *your* home is being sucked up by a hurricane.

● Where do you land?

● What do you see?

● Write your ideas here.

_____and

*child*

_____

*helper(s)*

_____

did this activity together

# Dress-up

Imagine that you are going to a fancy dress party, where you have to dress up as a character from a book.

● What costume will you wear?

● Draw a picture of yourself in the costume on a separate piece of paper.

● Write a sentence about why you chose it.

*impact* WRITING HOMEWORK

# Teachers' Notes
## YEAR FOUR

**The time machine!** Talk about the times and places the children have chosen; why did they choose them? Has anyone chosen the same time or place as anyone else? Look at the different reasons the children give for their choices, and try sorting them into different categories. You could build your own time machines, planning the designs and drawing pictures to show what the children think they might see when they reach their destinations. Read some stories about time travel (or talk about them if you think the style might be too adult for your children). Put everyone's dates in chronological order; who chose to go the furthest back in time?

**Mega-menu** Read through the menus that the children have written; did anyone have any unusual things to eat? Pick up on any alliteration as this is often used in advertising slogans. Plan your own restaurant in the classroom – menus, ingredients, shopping lists, recipes – and then invite some special guests to your restaurant . Perhaps you could plan for it to open just before home time so the parents could come a little early and buy something to eat. The money could go towards a school outing or favourite charity.

**Magic book** Ask one of the children to explain all the things he or she would be aware of as the main character in the story. The 'story so far' will need to be summarised first. Perhaps the other children could guess which story the reader is talking about just from the description. This could be a good way to start 'hot seating' if you have not already tried it in your class. Choose a character from the story you are reading in class. Take the role of the character, and ask the children to ask you questions, answering for the character. Once the children have got the idea, they can take turns to answer questions in the role of a character themselves.

**Character diary** Read a few diary pages out to the class, and see if they can guess the character and the story. Read a story together and then ask the children to choose a character from the story and rewrite it in their own words (from that character's point of view).

**Character profile** Talk about the labelled pictures the children have brought in; has anyone profiled the same character as someone else? Collect the personality profiles and put them in a class book that the children can refer to when they are reading at school. Perhaps you could also make a book of the real characters in the class!

**Animal characters** Talk about the descriptions the children have brought in; has anyone described the same animal as someone else? Pick up on any alliteration that the children have used. Collect the animal characters and put them in a class book that the children can look at when they are reading at school.

**Breakfast noises** Collect the phrases the children have written down. You may want to point out any onomatopoeias they have used or invented. Use this collection as a basis for writing breakfast noises poems. An hilarious but graphic example is 'Shut your mouth when you're eating!' by Michael Rosen. It gives a wonderful example of the kinds of conversation that happen at mealtimes. You could extend this into a drama/music activity by making sound pictures of the children's poems using percussion instruments and the children's voices
*Quick, let's get out of here!* Michael Rosen (Puffin Books).

**Character tree** Before this activity goes home, make sure that the children have an understanding of what a family tree is. Afterwards, share the character trees the children have produced, and make pictorial versions with drawings of the characters as well as their names.

**Family anecdotes** This work can be used as a stimulus for drama. The children tell their funny stories to the others, using voice, face and body movements to accentuate funny moments. Alternatively, it can be used as a starting point for written work. Working in pairs, the children produce a report of the event for a class newspaper. One child is the reporter, who takes notes based on the other child's information and then writes it up.

**Heroic names** Collect all the names and make a list. Sort the names; yes, they are all 'heroic names' but what kind of heroic? Are they male or female, mythical or modern, real or imagined? Ask the children

to choose names they particularly like and write descriptions of those characters; what they look like, where they live, who their friends are, what they do on a daily basis. Try to think up some 'evil' character names that could be incorporated into the stories about the heroes. Use the storylines that the children come up with in subsequent drama sessions in small groups.

**Eye-witness report: Cinderella** Read a selection of the eye-witness reports and discuss how much they differ. Can the children account for these differences? How much is it to do with the version of the story that each child picked, and how much to do with their personal interpretations of the events that they 'saw'? Try this activity based on other well known fairy tales, i.e. *The Three Bears*.

**On the beat** Before this activity goes home, make sure you have read at least the beginning of the story of *Peter Pan* to the children. You may want to read a simplified or abridged version to them, so that they are not confused by the language. Draw pictures of what you think Peter Pan and the others look like. Make models of Never-Never Land, or draw maps.

**Baby talk** Encourage the children to give their babies names, and to write something about their families. What do the babies do all day? What sort of care do they need? Interview a mother who has a baby, and ask her questions about all the things a baby needs. Write a list of all the things which are essential if you have a baby in the house. Discuss the most annoying thing about living with a baby and the best thing. Write a few sentences about these.

**People profile 1/2/3** Read out a few of the profiles that the children have written; how do they vary? Have the children identified these imaginary characters with people they know, or even with themselves?

**Where's Papa going with that axe?**
Share some of the alternative storylines that the children have thought of, and look at the ways in which they have been set out. Has anyone used a storyboard or flowchart layout? How many happy endings are there? Do people prefer to write happy endings than sad ones? Encourage the children to flesh out the storylines, and read these new versions at story time.

*Charlotte's web* EB White (Hamish Hamilton)

**I share a bedroom and I hate it!**
Once you have collected all the complaints, try writing a collective poem on the subject of sharing a bedroom. The title of the activity provides quite a good refrain. Use a large sheet of paper pinned up at the front of the class so all the children can see. Write down the title of the activity as the first line, and ask the children to contribute phrases about their own experiences. Repeat the refrain every four or six lines. You may want to move a few lines around – ask the children what they think. They could then try to memorise the poem.

**Home helps** The children come back to school with two conflicting views; their parents' and their own! Talk about the jobs the children help with, and the jobs that parents think they should do. In a drama session, ask the children to try and think about things from their parents' point of view; what factors should they keep in mind? Ask pairs of children to take it in turns to

take on the role of the parent and the child – in a situation where the parent is complaining about the lack of help in the house!

**You're *so* embarrassing!** This work can be used as a stimulus for drama activities where the children are given the opportunity to tell their funny stories (in the role of their parents) to the others. They should use voice, face and body movements to accentuate funnier moments in the story. Alternatively, it can be used as a starting point for some written work. Play the children a tape of one of Joyce Grenfell's famous monologues. Talk about why these were so funny, and encourage the children to try writing their own comedy monologues.

**The best and worst of school** Discuss the lists with the children. Is school a more pleasant experience now than it was for their parents? List the good and bad points about the school that you can all agree on, and draft some letters to the governors raising some of the issues with them. Perhaps you could invite one of them in to answer your questions.

**The things you wear!** Discuss the lists with the children. Do they wear any clothes that their great-great-grandmothers might recognise? Discuss the way in which fashions have changed over time, and the things that have influenced those changes (the wars, new fabrics, changes in lifestyle). What kind of clothes do the children imagine their grandchildren could be wearing in the future?

**Some excuse!** Read the letters out and display them so all the children can read

them again. Have they remembered all the conventions of letter writing? Ask them to devise comic strips to go with their letters, telling the real reason why they missed the week of school!

*John Patrick Norman McHennessey* John Burningham (Cape)

**Junk mail** Display the children's leaflets alongside some real ones. Discuss the language that has been used, and the eye-catching designs. Which are the most effective? Which colours work best? Do any use rhymes or quotations? Pick up on any alliteration the children have used. You could take this a stage further by designing packaging for the sweets, and even television commercials using storyboards.

*Charlie and the chocolate factory* Roald Dahl (Puffin)

**A fitting name** Discuss the names that the children have thought of, and why they think those names suit them. Talk about the names of characters they have come across in their own reading; can they think of some names that have really suited their characters? Sort these names into categories such as good evil old young mythical modern. Give each child a chart with columns headed 'Type of character', 'Character name', and 'Character profile' so that they can think of their own names for a variety of characters and briefly give a description of their personalities.

**As old as Methuselah** Discuss the names that the children have thought of, and why they think those names suit old or young people. Talk about the names of characters they have come across in their own reading; can they think of some names

that have really suited their characters? Sort these names into categories such as good evil, old young, mythical, modern. Give each child a chart with columns headed 'Type of character', 'Character name', and 'Character profile' so that they can think of their own names for a variety of characters and briefly give a description of their personalities.

**What shall we wear?** Display the pictures that the children bring in. Discuss the clothes their helpers would like to dress them in; why did they choose those clothes? Do they want the children to dress more smartly or more sensibly? What do clothes say about people? Read out a detailed description of a character's appearance from a book the children are unfamiliar with without showing them any illustrations. Ask the children to draw pictures of the character, bearing in mind all the detail from the description, and write a personality profile. Compare the finished pictures and profiles, and discuss the differences and similarities.

# The time machine!

You have found the most amazing, incredible **time machine** ever!

● Which time will you go to?

● Will you go to the future or the past?

● Which place will you go to?

● Write down the time and the place.
These are the settings for your time machine.

● Tell your helper where you are going, and why.

**To the helper:**

● Talk about the time and place your child would like to go to. Help him or her to visualise what it might be like in the future or the past. If there is time, you could talk about the time and place you would like to go to and why.

**This activity draws on children's natural fascination with time travel. It will reinforce understanding of past, present and future and to help children to structure their own work in chronological sequence.**

_____and

*child*

_____

*helper(s)*

_____

did this activity together

_____and

*child*

_____

*helper(s)*

_____

did this activity together

# Mega-menu

● What did you eat for your last meal?

● Write a **menu** for your meal as if you were going to serve it in your restaurant. Make it sound as exciting and delicious as you can.

For example, fingers might become 'delicious fingers of fish in a crispy, crunchy coating, cooked to perfection'.

● You could decorate your menu, and make up a name for your restaurant!

# A magic book

Imagine that your book suddenly becomes a **magic book**. When you open it, you find yourself in the place where the story is set. You are standing right where the main character should be.

- What can you see?

- What can you smell?

- How do you feel?

- Are you afraid, worried, cheerful?

- Write down all the things that you notice on a piece of paper.

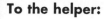

**To the helper:**

● Talk about the book your child is reading at the moment, and choose the page in which he or she would like to appear. Look at the illustrations carefully (if there are any), and read that part of the story again. Can you add any details? For example, you might suggest the noise of a plane passing overhead or a dog barking.

**This activity asks the child to write an account in the first person, based on empathy with a character. This is an important skill in imaginative writing.**

_____and

*child*

_____

*helper(s)*

_____

did this activity together

_____and

*child*

_____

*helper(s)*

_____

did this activity together

# Character diary

● Write a few pages of the **personal diary** of the main character from your story book.

Remember – this is a personal diary, so the writer would be writing down all his or her thoughts and feelings.

For example, whose diary might this be from?

'Well, what a day! It all started when Mum told me that Grandma was ill, and I should take some food to her in my basket...'

*impact* WRITING HOMEWORK

## Character profile

Think of the main **character** in your story.

Build up a personality profile of him or her.

- What does he or she look like?

- What clothes would he or she wear?

- What kind of a place would he or she live in?

- Does he or she have a car?

- What might be his or her favourite food or music?

- What would he or she watch on TV?

- Would he or she understand the music or programmes you like?

- Draw a picture of your character on a piece of paper.

- Show the things in the list above, and label them.

_____and

*child*

_____

*helper(s)*

_____

did this activity together

_____and

*child*

_____

*helper(s)*

_____

did this activity together

# Animal characters

● Can you think of some good words to describe some interesting animals?

A **snake** might be 'sly, sneaky, slithery'.

A **wolf** might be 'dangerous, fierce, sharp-toothed.

● Write down descriptions for at least three interesting animals on a piece of paper.

● Ask you helper to try a few – can you guess animals from their descriptions?

# Letters to characters

● Write a **letter** to your favourite character in your story.

● What might you want to say to him or her.

● Would you like to give some advice, or ask some questions about things that are not clear in the story?

● Try telling your helper about your story – it may help you to think of some questions.

_____and

*child*

_____

*helper(s)*

_____

did this activity together

_____and

*child*

_____

*helper(s)*

_____

did this activity together

# Breakfast noises

● What **noises** can you hear when you are eating your breakfast?

● Write a poem on a piece of paper using the noises that you hear.

# Character trees

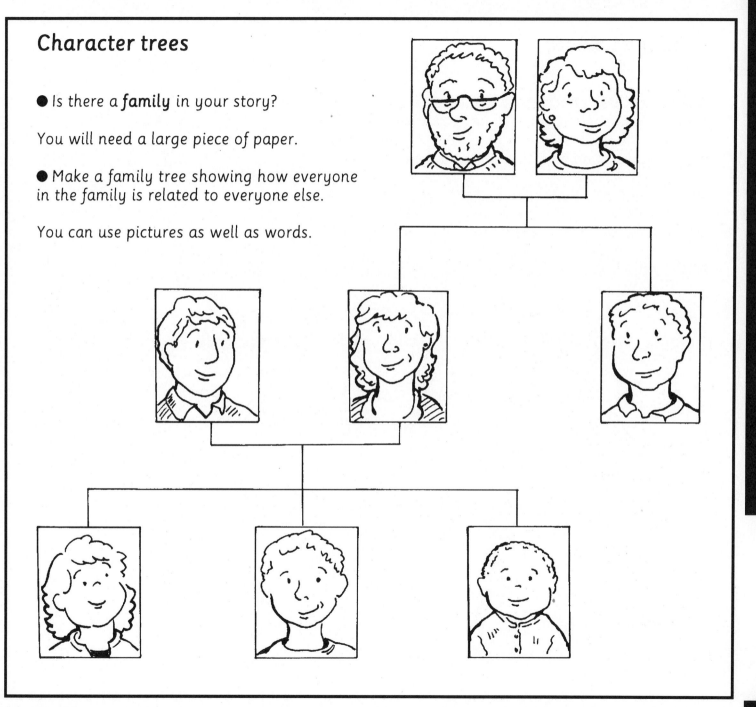

● Is there a **family** in your story?

You will need a large piece of paper.

● Make a family tree showing how everyone in the family is related to everyone else.

You can use pictures as well as words.

**To the helper:**

● You will need to talk carefully about the story, and all the characters mentioned in it.
● You may need to help with setting out the family tree, especially if there are uncles, aunts, nieces and nephews!

**A family tree is a way of organising and summarising information in graphic form – an important skill for the writer. This activity also leads to some very interesting discussions about the author's perspective . Whose 'side' is he or she on, and does it make a difference to the story?**

_____and

*child*

_____

*helper(s)*

_____

did this activity together

_____and

*child*

_____

*helper(s)*

_____

did this activity together

# Family anecdotes

● Do you know a good story about something that really happened to someone in your **family**?

● Ask people at home if they know any stories.

● Try to find one that will make people laugh, or will be very exciting.

● Write it down as it was told to you – use the same words if you can!

● Write the best story down on a piece of paper.

*impact* WRITING HOMEWORK

# Heroic names

- Think of some names for some really **heroic characters** who could feature in an adventure story. Make them as original as possible!

- Write down the best five names here.

**To the helper:**

- Talk with your child about stories you have heard or read with really heroic characters in them, for example *Flash Gordon* or *Girl Hero*. This should spark off some ideas for new names.

**Characterisation is an important aspect of imaginative writing, and creating a character's name helps to develop personality. Back at school we shall flesh out these characters so that they can feature in our stories.**

_____and

*child*

_____

*helper(s)*

_____

did this activity together

_____and

*child*

_____

*helper(s)*

_____

did this activity together

# Eye-witness report: Cinderella

An eye witness is a person who was on the scene of a crime or other event, and saw exactly what happened.

● Imagine you were standing outside Prince Charming's castle just as Cinderella rushed out at midnight!

You have been asked by the police to write down everything that you saw and heard.

● Write your report on a piece of paper.

# On the beat

An eye witness is a person who was on the scene of a crime or other event, and saw exactly what happened.

● Imagine you were a police officer on the beat at night when the Darling children were taken by Peter Pan...

You have been asked to write down in your own words everything that you saw and heard.

● Write your report on a piece of paper.

_____and

*child*

_____

*helper(s)*

_____

did this activity together

# Baby talk

Imagine you are a baby .

You are going to the shops in your buggy.

● What can you see?

● What can you hear?

● What are you thinking?

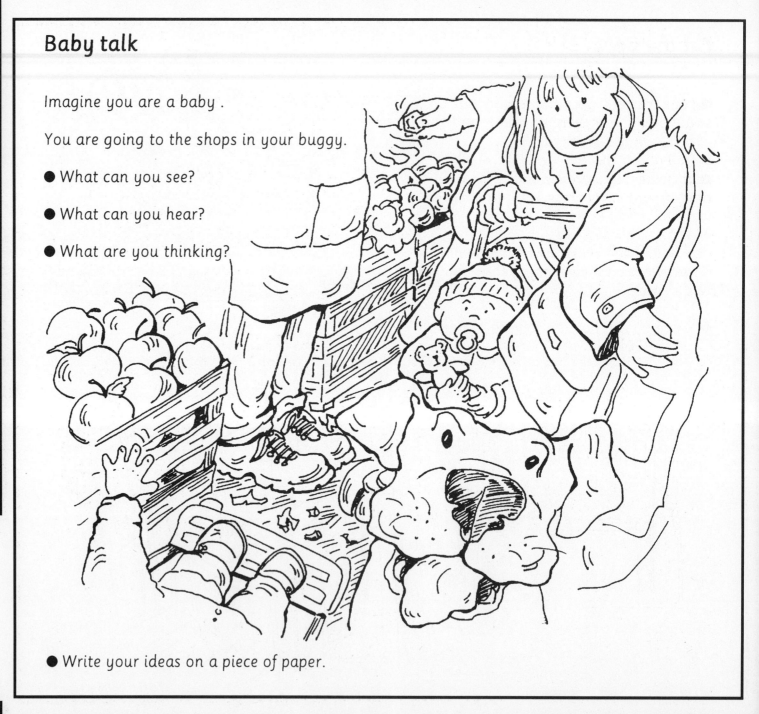

● Write your ideas on a piece of paper.

# People's profile 1

● Read the following description of a fictional **character**.

● Talk about the character with your helper, and discuss what kind of person this might be.

● When you have built up a picture in your mind, write down at least four sentences describing him or her on a piece of paper.

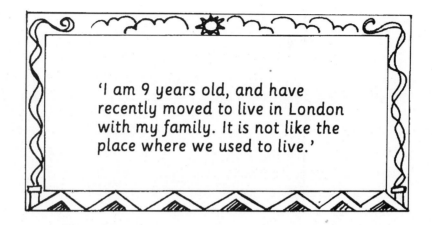

'I am 9 years old, and have recently moved to live in London with my family. It is not like the place where we used to live.'

**To the helper:**

● When you discuss this person, try to draw as many parallels as you can with your own child's experience: Has he or she ever moved house?

● Is this character a boy or a girl? Where do you imagine he or she has moved from – another big city or a village perhaps.

● The idea is to create as many details as possible about this imaginary person; in effect to tell a story about him or her.

**You are both working to create a context for an imaginary character. This is an important skill, employed to construct realistic characters in story writing.**

_____ and

*child*

_____

*helper(s)*

_____

did this activity together

_____and

_child_

_____

_helper(s)_

_____

did this activity together

# People profile 2

● Read the following description of a fictional **character**.

● Talk about the character with your helper, and discuss what kind of person this might be.

● When you have built up a picture in your mind, write down at least four sentences describing him or her on a piece of paper.

'I am 17 years old and have no job. I spend most of my time with my mates. I'm a keen Leeds United fan.'

# People profile 3

- Read the following description of a fictional **character**.

- Talk about the character with your helper, and discuss what kind of person this might be

- When you have built up a picture in your mind, write down at least four sentences describing him or her on a piece of paper.

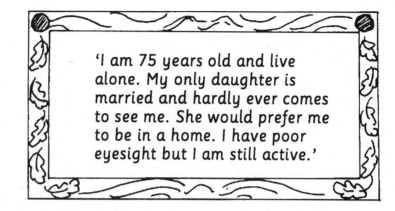

'I am 75 years old and live alone. My only daughter is married and hardly ever comes to see me. She would prefer me to be in a home. I have poor eyesight but I am still active.'

_____and
*child*

_____
*helper(s)*

_____
did this activity together

_____and

*child*

_____

*helper(s)*

_____

did this activity together

# Where's Papa going with that axe?

● Read the book **Charlotte's Web**.

At the beginning, Fern asks the question above.

● Can you invent an outline for another story which begins with that line? Write your ideas below.

● Try to use the same characters.

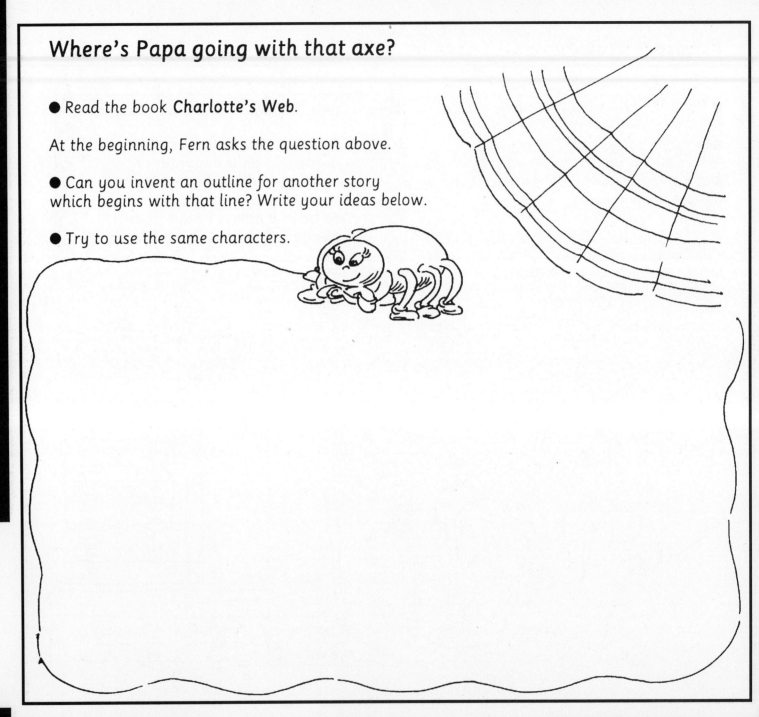

# I share a bedroom and I hate it!

● Do you have to **share** anything with a brother or sister?

● How do you feel about it?

● Write down the things you would prefer not to share in the space opposite!

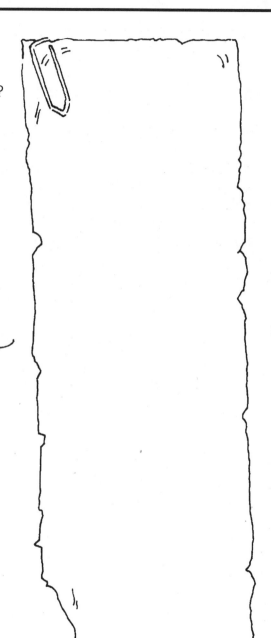

**To the helper:**

● Talk about the house, and the way in which personal space is arranged.

**Domestic complaints are a good source of inspiration for writing stories and poetry. Children can draw on strong feelings which they have experienced personally, to produce convincing text.**

_____and

*child*

_____

*helper(s)*

did this activity together

_____and

*child*

_____

*helper(s)*

_____

did this activity together

# Home helps

● Do you think you should **help around the house**?

● Which jobs should children do?

● Which jobs can children do safely?

● Write down what you think on a piece of paper.

● Ask your helper to write down what he or she thinks!

# You're **SO** embarrassing!

● Ask your Mum or Dad or your helper to tell you about some of the times you've embarrassed them in public.

● Write down the funniest examples on a piece of paper!

**To the helper:**

● Talk about your memories of embarrassing incidents with children. Ask a number of people for their funny stories.

● If the best story involves people talking, check whether the speech marks are being used correctly, and if not, give a hand with them.

**Embarrassing memories conjure up strong feelings which we can all identify with. Drawing on these feelings helps children to produce convincing, imaginative writing. We shall share our school memories and expand them into full-length embarrassment stories!**

_____and

*child*

_____

*helper(s)*

_____

did this activity together

_____and

*child*

_____

*helper(s)*

_____

did this activity together

# The best and worst of school

● Which things **do you enjoy** at school?

● Which things **don't you enjoy**?

● Talk to your helper. Which things did he or she enjoy at school?

● What things did he or she not enjoy?

● Write four lists:

The things I enjoy at school

The things I don't enjoy at school

The things my helper enjoyed at school

The things my helper didn't enjoy at school

# The things you wear!

● Imagine that your great-great grandmother comes to tidy your bedroom!

You show her your clothes.

● Are there some things that she wouldn't recognise?

● Make a list on a piece of paper.

**To the helper:**

● Talk about your child's great-great-grandmother. Do you know her name? Can you find any photos of her?

● Clothes have changed drastically since our great-great-grandmothers were alive. Can you find any pictures of 19th century fashions?

**Making lists is an important skill which helps children to organise their writing, particularly non-fiction. Back in class we will discuss the information gathered and talk about how fashions have changed. We shall then imagine what people will wear in the future.**

_____and

*child*

_____

*helper(s)*

_____

did this activity together

**To the helper:**

● Read the story of *John Patrick Norman McHennessey;* what are all the wonderful excuses that he comes up with?

● You may need to help your child to set out the letter.

**It is important for children to learn the conventions of letter writng. We shall use these imaginative letters back at school to write more tall stories.**

_____and

*child*

_____

*helper(s)*

_____

did this activity together

## Some excuse!

Oh, no! you got the dates of half term wrong and ended up missing a week of school!

● Write a letter to your teacher with your helper. Make up an elaborate excuse about why you missed a week of school.

# Junk mail

- Do you get lots of advertising leaflets through your door?

- Design a leaflet to advertise a new sweet.

_____and

*child*

_____

*helper(s)*

_____

did this activity together

**To the helper:**

● Discuss your child's personality; they may not be aware of certain 'qualities'!

● You could make up a name like the ones the American Indians used; for example, 'Fierce Bear' for someone with a temper. Or you could use the name of a Greek god, or famous person.

**Names are an integral part of character and character development. By thinking about their own personalities, and by listening to other's views, children will gain a better idea of how best to name their story characters.**

_____and

*child*

_____

*helper(s)*

_____

did this activity together

# A fitting name

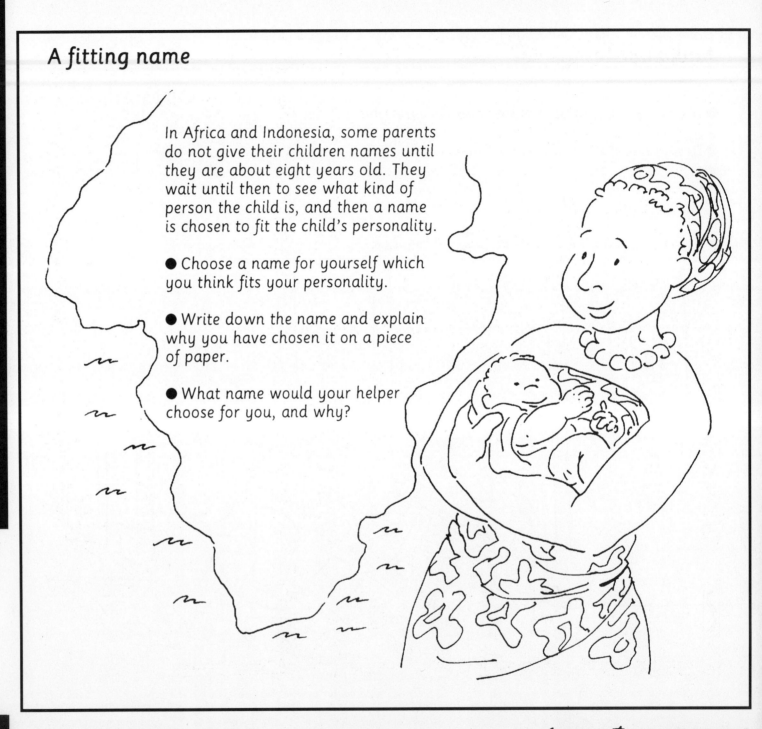

In Africa and Indonesia, some parents do not give their children names until they are about eight years old. They wait until then to see what kind of person the child is, and then a name is chosen to fit the child's personality.

● Choose a name for yourself which you think fits your personality.

● Write down the name and explain why you have chosen it on a piece of paper.

● What name would your helper choose for you, and why?

*impact* WRITING HOMEWORK

# As old as Methuselah

Some Innuit tribes give themselves new names when they grow old. They say it makes them feel young again.

● What names do you think are **'young'** names?

● What names do you think are **'old'** names?

● In the space provided make a list of names that would suit old people, and a list of names that would suit young people.

**'Old' names**

**'Young' names**

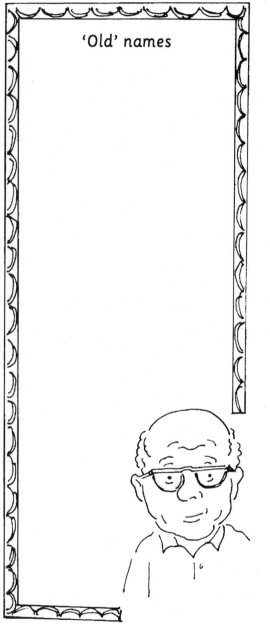

**To the helper:**

● Talk about the names of people you know.
● Talk about old-fashioned names and new names such as River (Phoenix).

**Names are an integral part of character and character development. By thinking about what they consider to be 'old' or 'young' names, and by listening to other people's views, children will gain a better idea of how to name their story characters appropriately.**

_____and

*child*

_____

*helper(s)*

_____

did this activity together

_____and

*child*

_____

*helper(s)*

_____

did this activity together

# What shall we wear?

● Imagine that you can tell your helper what he or she should wear and why!

● Draw a picture of him or her, with labels describing each item of clothing.

● Ask your helper to draw a picture of what they would like to see you wearing!

# Teachers' Notes
## Y E A R   F I V E

**A fantastic film** Talk about the characters, settings and plots that the children have thought of. The children could build up their plots with screenplays, scene by scene (giving directions on what is seen as well as what is said). A good art/design activity is to build film sets. Give each child a cardboard box and cut away at least one of the sides and the top, leaving the back, the base and the sides for decoration. They could make Plasticine models for their characters and props – or perhaps they have some suitable dolls or figures at home.

**Space aliens!** Display the pictures the children have drawn, and discuss the different adaptations they have for their various climates and conditions. This could be linked with any work you have done about animals and their physiological adaptation to their environments. Imagine that your class has been given the privilege of being the first 'class in space'; where would you go to, and what would you see? Start the story off together, and then let the children write their own adventures.

**New endings** Read out a few of the children's stories, and discuss how they have managed to get from the original

storylines; how else could they have changed them? Are the children happy with their versions, or do they still prefer the originals? Why? Try finishing the stories, starting from the point where the children intervened in the storylines.

**New endings 2** Ask the children to write out their version in the form of storyboards. These could be displayed near the book area so that the other children can read them and compare them with the original text as the story develops.

**Letters to writers** Read out the letters the children have written. Perhaps you could post some of them (care of the publisher) and see if you get any replies. You may be able to arrange for a children's author to visit the school. He or she could then answer some of the questions the children have asked in their letters.

**Gossip** Share the stories that the children have written; who has the funniest one? Try working with some traditional stories or myths, guessing what the original versions might have been! Read the children a couple of 'true' stories from the local newspaper. Can they elaborate on these stories and turn them into much more exciting or spectacular events?

Ask them to write down their new versions and display them around the original newspaper reports.

**Circular stories** This is an old circular story: 'It was a dark and stormy night and the rain was coming down in torrents. The robbers were sitting round their camp fire. One of the robbers said, "Tell us a story, Chief." So the chief began, "It was a dark and stormy night and the rain..."' Read the children's circular stories. Can they draw them as a series of cartoons so that they can be displayed in a circle?

**Who wrote that?** Look at the funny titles and authors that the children have thought of; perhaps you could display them as a fake bookshelf, with the spines visible. How many children have managed to incorporate a pun? Read *Harry's mad* by Dick King-Smith with the children, and discuss the use of puns to convey a range of meanings. Collect the puns that the children have used, and try to think of some others. Try writing a sentence using one or two of the puns to create a word picture.
*Harry's mad* Dick King-Smith (Puffin Books)

**Meaningful names** Collect all the names and their meanings, and make a class book or wall display. Don't forget to include your own name! You could make a kind of illustrated register.

**Nicknames** Discuss the children's nicknames. Which do they think are appropriate? Which are funny? Give the children a list of characters from films or stories such as *Dick Whittington, Aladdin, Robin Hood* – and ask them to choose one and invent a nickname for him or her. They must then draw the character,

write the nickname and write about why it is appropriate.

**Here is the news!** When the children bring their funny news items back into class, ask them to choose the best ones. Set up a table at the front of the class as a newsdesk. You may want to provide an old pair of glasses without lenses as a piece of optional costume. Ask the children to take turns to be the newsreader. Encourage them to assume the role of a real newsreader, with the appropriate posture, attitude and tone of voice. The more serious they appear when they are reading, the funnier it will be! Alternatively, you could turn everyone's favourite stories into a funny newspaper for everyone to read.

**Private names** Talk with the children about their ideas. Find out some more about Canadian Indians; what other beliefs do they have? Write stories about names – special secret names that should not be shared.

**A mono-dialogue!** Before this activity goes home, play the children an excerpt from a Joyce Grenfell recording as an example of a comic monologue.

Discuss different settings for this type of writing: for example, a sales assistant in a shop, a dentist talking to a patient, or a driving instructor talking to his or her pupil. Read out a few examples of the children's monologues when they come back into class. Can the others guess what the other person is saying? Why is it funnier not to hear what the other person is saying?

**You should have been there when...** Ask a few children to read out or, preferably, to tell their stories. Discuss the fact that stories can sound much more interesting if they are written down in the style in which we might tell them. Story openings can be particularly boring if they are always written in the same style. However, the spoken version can capture the imagination and interest much more quickly and effectively, for example, 'I had just shut my eyes for a moment when...', or 'You know, what I really hate is...' or 'Well, we were all in the garden some time last summer when...', and so on.

**It wasn't my fault!** Ask one of the children to read out his or her version of the story, and then ask the rest of the class to vote on whether or note the child was unfairly blamed. Once the vote has been cast, ask the child to read the helper's version of events. How many children change their minds? Talk about the term 'objective' and 'subjective'. Is it possible to tell any story subjectively? Choose a story that is familiar to all the children, and ask them to try to write an objective account. It is more difficult that it seems!

**TV rules** Ask some of the children to read out their pieces of writing. Have they managed to express their opinions clearly? How do they manage to convince the listener? Play a role-play game with a few volunteers. Ask the children to choose from a selection of issues; one child then argues a particular point of view for, and the other against. Examples of issues might be 'We should only be allowed to bring healthy food to school', or 'We should be allowed to watch television in the playtimes at school', or 'Children should be allowed to decide what time they want to go to bed'.

**Guess what happened to me!** Collect the stories and choose favourites. Can the children tell which sentences were written by helpers and which by the children?

**Roller-coaster** Display the children's rides, alongside their descriptions and names. If you have the space, you could plan your own theme park. What will the park be called? Will it have themed areas? Design a range of rides and attractions suitable for the whole family. Draw a map or build a model of your theme park.

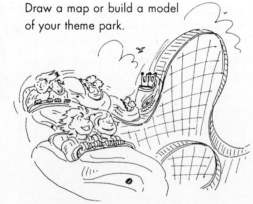

**Worst book** Make a class list of the features of a good book and the features of a bad book. Ask the children to choose some examples of good books.

Can they write a short review of one they think is particularly good? You can then make a collection of book reviews which will help others when choosing a book.

**Superhero** Before this activity goes home, make sure that the children are familiar with the kind of description you are looking for. Perhaps you could borrow some hero cards which come with packets of bubble gum – these tend to have a picture of the hero on one side of the card and some background on the other. When the children bring back their descriptions, pair them up and ask each pair to write a story in which both of their superheroes star. Are they working together, or against one another?

**Saturday morning television** The children could read one another's instructions, and choose the best game. Then they could draft letters to the producers of the Saturday morning programmes to sell them the idea – they will need to make the game sound as entertaining as possible.

**Revolting ice cream!** Collect all the descriptive vocabulary into a word bank that the children can refer to when writing. Ask the children to write stories featuring the disgusting ice creams and the characters they have suggested to eat them. *Fungus the bogeyman* Raymond Briggs (Hamish Hamilton)

**The magic casserole dish** Look at some picture books written for younger children. Point out how the story progresses gradually, with lots of illustration to help tell the story. Ask the children to turn their stories into picture books for the younger ones.

**School years** Discuss which arrangement would suit everyone best – can you all agree on one plan? Does anyone have a particularly persuasive argument? Has anyone considered the effect on teachers, school caretakers or working parents? Draft letters to the school governors with your suggestions.

**Up above or down below** Display the phrases the children have thought of. You could use painted backdrops representing the two environments.Put the two displays up next to each other. Write stories from the point of view of a fish or a bird. It might be interesting to start from the same point for both, for example, an underwater volcano erupting, or a hot air balloon crashing into the sea.

**Elephant roadblock** It would be fun to use the children's ideas as the starting point for the 'Road user's handbook for all eventualities'! Can you think of any other unlikely incidents that might happen to you as you go about your daily travels? Ask the children to write down their ideas.

**What am I?** Illustrate the descriptions and make them into a class book. Extend this into a consideration of riddles, which are highly detailed descriptions incorporating a paradox of some kind. Make a collection of riddles.

# A fantastic film

Imagine that you are going to make a film!

It is going to be an adventure story.

- On a piece of paper, write a description of the place in which your story is set.

- Write down the names of three of the characters you will have in your film.

- Write down what happens at the beginning, in the middle and at the end.

_____ and
**child**

_____
**helper(s)**

_____

did this activity together

_____and

*child*

_____

*helper(s)*

_____

did this activity together

# Space aliens!

● Write profiles of three **'aliens'** from other planets.

● Which planets are they from?

● Describe what they look like.

● Draw on a piece of paper pictures of them and explain the reasons for their physical features. (For example, do they have antennae, and if so, what are they for?)

# New endings 1

● In your next reading book, go as far as the middle and then stop.

● Go back one page. What might have happened, instead of what you have just read?

● Write your idea down on a piece of paper.

● Read the two versions to your helper. Can your helper guess which ending is which? Which ending does he or she prefer?

● Now illustrate your page. Try to draw in the same style as the book illustrations!

_____and

*child*

_____

*helper(s)*

_____

did this activity together

_____and

*child*

_____

*helper(s)*

_____

did this activity together

# New endings 2

● Think about the story your teacher is reading in class.

● What do you think is going to happen next?

● Talk to your helper and to other people about the story.

● Write down what you think is going to happen in the next few chapters.

● Write down how you think the story will end.

● You could draw a picture to go with your writing.

# Letters to writers

● Write a **letter to the author** of your reading book.
Ask questions about where the ideas came from.

● Ask about the illustrations; who chose the
illustrator and why was that person chosen?

● Remember to set the letter out properly!

**To the helper:**

● You may need to help your child to set out the letter.

**This activity reinforces the conventions of letter writing, and focuses attention on writing for a specific audience. The child will have to think carefully about the whole book; characters, plot, setting, illustrations, in order to ask relevant questions.**

_____and

*child*

_____

*helper(s)*

_____

did this activity together

_____and

*child*

_____

*helper(s)*

_____

did this activity together

# Gossip

Gossip can make an event grow from something fairly ordinary into something quite out of the ordinary!

As one person retells a story to the next person, parts can become exaggerated and parts can be left out, and so it changes into a very different story.

● Write down the story of something simple that happened to you, and then write down how the story might change if a chain of gossips were to get hold of it!

# Circular stories

● Write a story that goes round in a circle, ending up back at the beginning.

Here is an example:

Billy jumped up, brushed himself off, and strode down the lane. As he approached the bend he heard the screeching of brakes, and before he knew what had happened... BANG!... he was flat on his back looking up at a very embarrassed cyclist.

_____and

*child*

_____

*helper(s)*

_____

did this activity together

_____and

*child*

_____

*helper(s)*

_____

did this activity together

# Who wrote that?

Some books are written by very appropriate authors!

Here are two examples:
**Aspirin and its uses** by Ivor Headache
**The book of transport** by Orson Cart

● Think of some more ideas, and write them down.

# Meaningful names

● Does your **name** mean anything?

For example, 'Zoe' means 'life', and 'Fred' means 'Peace'.

● Try and find out what your name means, or make up a meaning for it and write it in the space opposite.

● Do the same for your helper's name, and for someone else in your family.

**To the helper:**

● Do you have a book of babies' names? This might be useful for looking up the meanings.

● Can you remember, or do you know, why your child's name was chosen? Did your parents ever tell you why they chose your name? Do your names come from a country other than Britain?

**Names are an integral part of character and character development. By finding out more about what names mean, and the reasons why people choose certain names, children will gain an insight into how to name their own characters.**

_____and

*child*

_____

*helper(s)*

_____

did this activity together

_____and

*child*

_____

*helper(s)*

_____

did this activity together

# Nicknames

● Have you got a **nickname**?

● Write a short story explaining how you got your nickname, or how someone you know got his or her nickname.

*impact* WRITING HOMEWORK

# Here is the news!

● Make up a couple of humorous news items.

Your helper could write one, too.

**To the helper:**

● Talk about humorous news items you have heard in the past. These are the items that tend to get read out last, for example, the donkey who had a taste for his neighbour's washing, or the cat who adopted a family of ducklings.

**Writing a story in the style of a television or newspaper report gives the children experience in using a particular form of writing. Back in school, we will dramatise the reports and possibly turn them into a newspaper.**

_____and

*child*

_____

*helper(s)*

_____

did this activity together

_____and

*child*

_____

*helper(s)*

_____

did this activity together

# Private names

Some Canadian Indians think that it is very dangerous to give their names to strangers.

● Why do you think this is?

● Discuss it with your helper, and write your ideas on a piece of paper.

# A mono-dialogue!

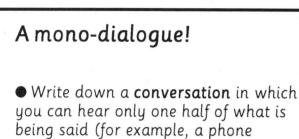

● Write down a **conversation** in which you can hear only one half of what is being said (for example, a phone conversation).

● Work with your helper to make the conversation as funny as possible!

**To the helper:**

● This is a technique frequently used by comedians and writers.
● If this requires a lot of writing, you could give a hand by acting as a scribe.

**Writing or reading one half of a conversation requires the writer or reader to imagine what is being said by the other person. This activity will help children to construct realistic dialogues in their own imaginative writing. Back at school we shall share our 'mono-dialogues'. Did we all imagine the same words for the other half of the conversation?**

_____and

*child*

_____

*helper(s)*

_____

did this activity together

_____and

*child*

_____

*helper(s)*

_____

did this activity together

# You should have been there when...

● Have you ever seen something funny or unusual, and wished someone else was there to see it too?

● On a piece of paper, write about an event which you wish someone else had seen.

● Ask your helper to do the same.

# It wasn't my fault!

● Have you ever been blamed by your helper for something you didn't do?

● Choose an incident when this happened to you and write about it from your point of view.

● Ask your helper to write about it from the opposite point of view.

**To the helper:**

● Talk about the incident and remember what you can about it. (Try not to get into an argument!)

**Everyone is a storyteller; we are constantly telling one another stories about ourselves, or people we know. The home can be a rich source of stories, and everyone will have a different version. The idea behind this activity is to capture two people's versions of one particular story. This will make the child focus on bias in writing (the fact that almost all accounts are subjective). We will share these stories back at school.**

_____and

*child*

_____

*helper(s)*

_____

did this activity together

_____and

_child_

_____

_helper(s)_

_____

did this activity together

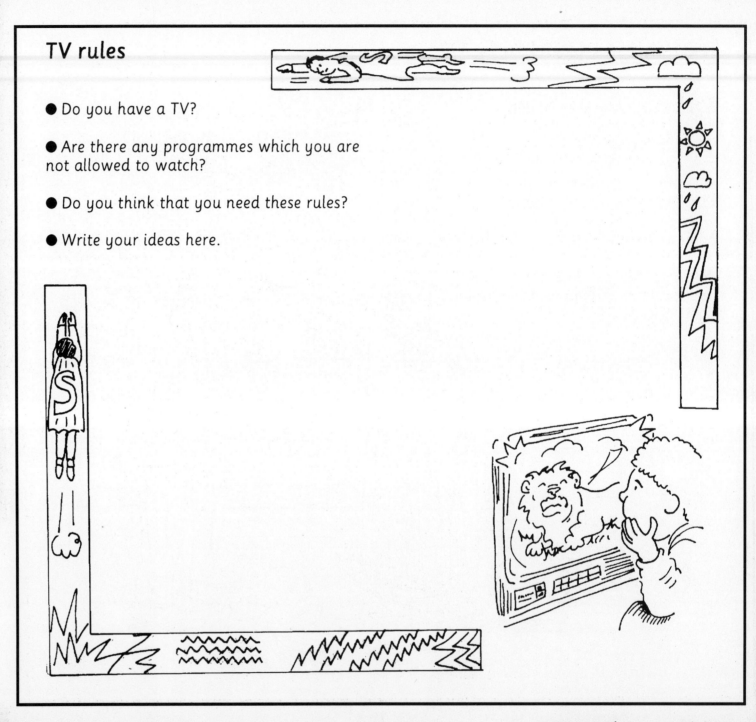

# TV rules

● Do you have a TV?

● Are there any programmes which you are not allowed to watch?

● Do you think that you need these rules?

● Write your ideas here.

# Guess what happened to me!

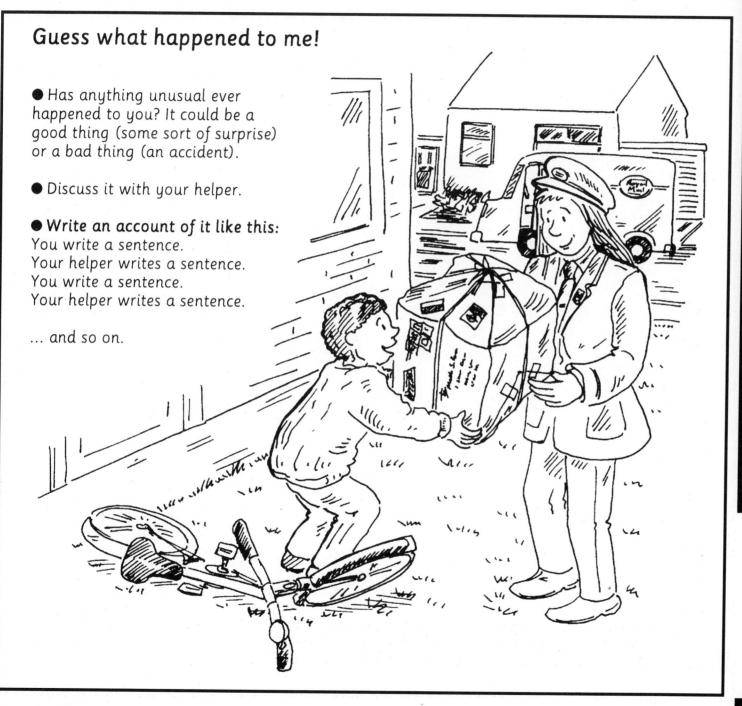

- Has anything unusual ever happened to you? It could be a good thing (some sort of surprise) or a bad thing (an accident).

- Discuss it with your helper.

- **Write an account of it like this:**
You write a sentence.
Your helper writes a sentence.
You write a sentence.
Your helper writes a sentence.

... and so on.

_____and

*child*

_____

*helper(s)*

_____

did this activity together

_____and

*child*

_____

*helper(s)*

_____

did this activity together

# Roller-coaster

● Design a really fast roller-coaster.

● Draw your ride and write a description. Give it a really exciting name, for example **'The Bat'** or **'The Edge'**.

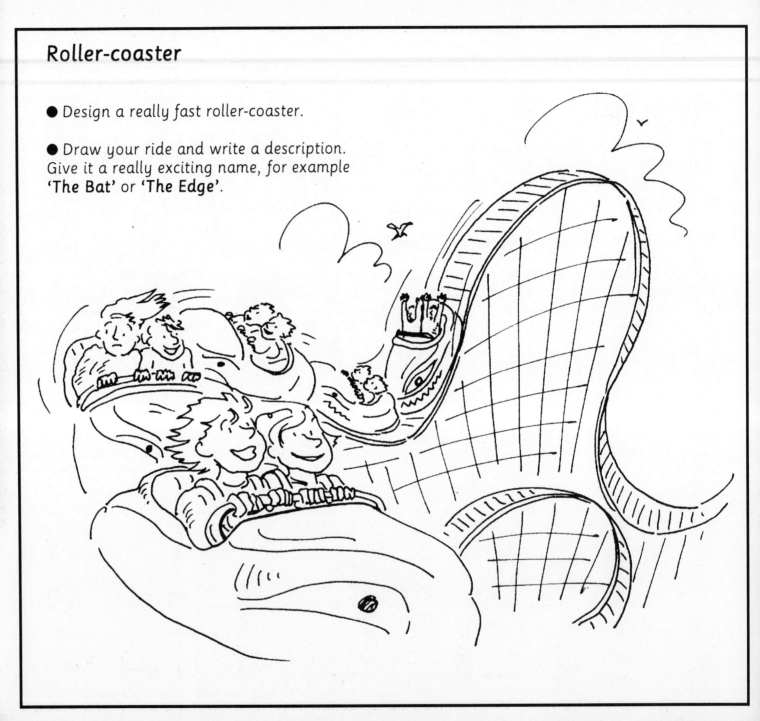

## Worst book

● Which is the worst book you have ever read?

● Write down the reasons why the book was so bad. Was it the style the author used? Do you find all books by this author difficult to read? Was it the plot, or were the characters unconvincing?

**To the helper:**

● Talk about the books your child likes to read. Which genres and authors does he or she prefer? Which books does he or she dislike, and why?

**Being able to identify different genres and the reasons why they prefer one genre over another is a useful skill both for when the children are choosing their own reading material and for when they are writing. It might help them to attempt to write different story types.**

_____and

*child*

_____

*helper(s)*

_____

did this activity together

_____and

*child*

_____

*helper(s)*

_____

did this activity together

# Superhero

● Invent a new **superhero**.

● Draw a picture and write a paragraph about your superhero.

● Does he or she have any special powers?

# Saturday morning television

● Design a game suitable for a children's Saturday morning TV programme. Draw a plan of the layout of the game, and write a description of how to play and how to win.

Most of these games involve much running around, a 'gunk tank', balloons and large plastic or foam props. They also tend to be based on a certain theme. For example, a prince has to steal the gold from a dragon in order to release the princess from the evil troll who has kidnapped her. Players are often dressed in rather ungainly costume and the courses may include several slippery slopes, ravines and all other types of obstacle. The idea is to collect as much gold as possible in the time allowed (one piece of gold allowed for every trip), each 'prince' competing against the others.

_____and

*child*

_____

*helper(s)*

_____

did this activity together

_____and

*child*

_____

*helper(s)*

_____

did this activity together

# Revolting ice cream!

● Design a new flavour of ice cream – maybe a disgusting one!

● Write down the name of the ice cream in the box, and the name of a person who might like to eat it (a real person or a character from a book).

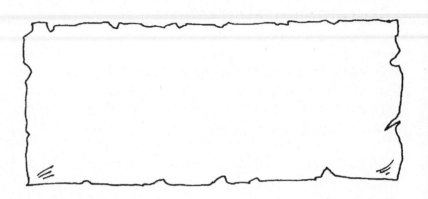

# The magic casserole dish

● Imagine that a family with no money to buy food has been given a magic casserole dish in return for a favour.

It seems to be empty, but when you command it with the magic words, it starts to work.
It will only stop if you say some more, slightly different, magic words.

● Write down what you think the favour was, and what the magic words were.

_____and

*child*

_____

*helper(s)*

_____

did this activity together

_____and

*child*

_____

*helper(s)*

_____

did this activity together

# School years

Children have to be in school for 39 weeks in each year. Could the holidays be arranged differently? For example, would you like to have two or four terms instead of the usual three? Would you continue with half-termly breaks?

● Redesign the school year, putting the holidays in a different place.

● Why do you think your way would be better? Write your ideas down on a piece of paper.

# Up above or down below?

- Imagine you are a **bird** flying high in the sky, or a **fish** swimming deep in the ocean.

- Write some phrases describing what it is like.

- Draw a picture to illustrate your phrases.

_____ and

*child*

_____

*helper(s)*

_____

did this activity together

_____and

*child*

_____

*helper(s)*

_____

did this activity together

# Elephant roadblock

Imagine that you and someone in your family are driving along in a car. You come round a corner, and WOW! There are three **elephants** blocking the road! There doesn't seem to be anyone else around. How do you persuade them to move?

● Write down your plan of action.

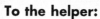

# What am I?

'Piece of furniture comprising lengths of wood arranged vertically and horizontally with a horizontal plane of approximately 90cm square.'

● Would you recognise this as the description of a chair?

● Write your own highly detailed description of a household object.

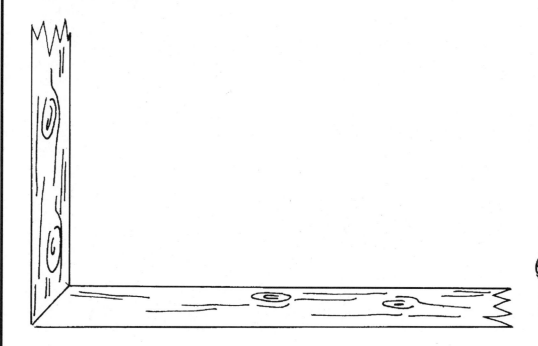

_____and

*child*

_____

*helper(s)*

_____

did this activity together

# Teachers' Notes
## YEAR SIX

**Magic time TV** Make a time capsule to be opened ten years or more into the future. Include a photograph of the class, and ask the children to write down how they hope the world will have changed for the better. You could also write time travel adventures where the children are whisked ten years into the future, meeting themselves as they would be in ten years' time. Imagine the kind of conversation that might occur.

**The story pyramid** Display the story pyramids in the book corner or near the library, so everyone can refer to them when they are next choosing a book. Put some time aside each day to discuss one of the pyramids; interview each child about his or her pyramid and the book to which it relates.

**Genres** Look at the variety of genres that the children have discovered. How may are there? What are the children's favourite genres? Is there a class favourite? Read a book that is clearly in one genre with the whole class. Discuss the features that make it that genre. Try writing stories in that genre as a class.

**Cola design** Design posters using the information the children have written at home. You may find that they want to make scale models of the colas, complete with packaging. Display the posters alongside the adverts. Which cola looks the most attractive? Use the children in the class to assess advertising campaigns or invite members of a parallel class or a younger class to assess them for you.

**Oh, No!** Display the cartoons on the wall so everyone can enjoy them. Ask the children to retell their stories in the most interesting way they can. Encourage them to use their whole bodies, including their faces to express the emotions and thoughts going through their head at the time.

**Future world** Read a time travel book such as *Tom's midnight garden*. Share everyone's ideas about the future, and write stories about travelling to the future. What are the improvements in the quality of life?

*Tom's midnight garden* Philippa Pearce (Puffin Books)

**Job names** Share the children's ideas. What is the point of changing the name of a job? Does it give the jobholder more status or more respect? Does it disguise negative aspects of the job? Does it change the job itself?

**Computer characters** Share the children's ideas. Do any of the games feature violence? Is it necessary? Ask the children to write up their plots in the form of storyboards, so that the changes in scenery can be seen. The children could use the computer to draw pictures of their characters and their settings. You could write letters to computer game manufacturers persuading them to buy your ideas!

**One day my Mum...** Read out a few of the children's dialogues. Perhaps you could read one as a play, and act out the argument. Try doing some role play in your next drama session – provide children with a role each, and a subject for them to disagree on. They must try and argue in character. For example, a parent and child may be having an argument about bedtimes, or someone may be trying to talk a vegetarian into trying some hamburger.

**Think bubbles** Talk about the children's cartoons. In what kinds of situation do people say one thing and mean another? Is it sometimes the best thing to do? Write stories about someone who has promised to say what he or she is thinking all day.

**I am what I wear** Display the pictures that the children bring in. Why did they choose those clothes? What do clothes say about you? Have a competition for the funniest or the best outfit!

**Parents on trial** Discuss the children's lists and see if you can reach agreement as a class about which of the restrictions are reasonable. Develop the lists into pieces of writing about new improved domestic scenarios!

**Designer labels** Discuss the different designer labels that the children have mentioned. Look through some newspapers and magazines for the corresponding advertising material. If you can, video some adverts from the television. What are the images saying? What do the manufacturers want us to think about their products? Look through some magazines which test the quality of the different products against one another. Is it really the quality that you are buying, or is it the image? Ask the children to write down how they see themselves, describing the kinds of clothes they like to wear, and why.

**Pass it on** Collect the reviews into a class book which can be added to and referred to when the children are choosing books.

**Remember me!** Ask the children to read out their obituaries, and talk about what they would like to be remembered for. Write obituaries for friends; what are their best qualities, and what would they like to be remembered for? Look at other styles of announcement such as those for weddings and births. Look at the book *The jolly postman*; you can find many different styles of announcement and letter writing here.

Perhaps you could write obituaries or other announcements for both characters.
*The jolly postman* Allan and Janet Ahlberg (Heinemann)

**A theme ball** Use one of the themes as the basis for a play. What happens? Who are the characters? Why are they having a ball? Read a selection of traditional stories where grand balls feature. Alternatively, children could imagine that they are reporters following a famous personality due to make an appearance at the ball. What do they see?

**Yuck!** Collect all the words into a word bank that the children can refer to. Ask them to write stories in which their disgusting food combinations feature. Can they include their story characters. *Fungus the bogeyman* Raold Dahl (Hamish Hamilton), *The hobbit* JRR Tolkein (Allen & Unwin)

**My ideal bedroom** Discuss the children's ideas. Construct models of the bedrooms from cut-away cardboard boxes. You could even decorate the bedrooms with the appropriate wallpaper or paint (the wallpaper could be from a sample book) and carpet (from samples or scraps). The children could imagine and plan

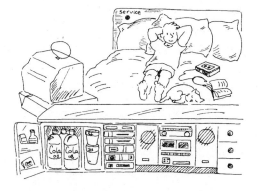

complete ideal homes from this starting point. Look at some estate agents' promotional material and ask the children to write about their ideal homes in this style; make them sound as attractive as possible!

**Cocktail** The children could design posters and other promotional material to go with their new drinks. Display the posters around the classroom – make sure children use the words they thought of to describe the drinks on the posters. Try making a few of the drinks, and tasting them. Are the children's descriptions accurate? Do their instructions work?

**Invent a pudding** The children could design posters and other promotional material to go with their newly made desserts. Display the posters around the classroom – make sure children use the words they thought of to describe the desserts on the posters. Try making a few of the desserts, and tasting them. Are the children's descriptions accurate? Do their instructions work?

**Wake-up Saturday TV** Look at all the children's plans together. What are the different themes? Look at some TV listings/

magazines, and then write articles that could go in a magazine to launch the new programmes. What information should go on Saturday's programme menu? Draft letters that could be sent to television producers to persuade them to buy the new programmes.

### What if ... children had the vote?

Ask some of the children to read out their ideas. Have they managed to express their opinions clearly? How do they manage to convince you? Play a role-play game with a few volunteers (some children may be rather nervous about doing this until they have seen a few others have a go). Ask the children to choose from a selection of issues, and then one child argues for and the other against the issue. You may need to explain that they may have to argue the opposite of something they themselves believe.

### What if ... only women had the vote?

Ask some of the children to read out their ideas. Have they managed to express their opinions clearly? How do they manage to convince you? Play a role-play game with a few volunteers . Ask the children to choose from a selection of issues, and then one child argues for and the other against the issue. You may need to explain that they may have to argue the opposite of something they themselves believe.

### What if ... eating meat were illegal?

Ask some of the children to read out their ideas. Have they managed to express their opinions clearly? How do they manage to convince you? Play a role-play game with a few volunteers (some children may be

rather nervous about doing this until they have seen a few others have a go). Ask the children to choose from a selection of issues, and then one child argues for and the other against the issue. You may need to explain that they may have to argue the opposite of something they believe.

**Family crest** Look at the children's family crests; display them alongside the information they have written. Look at a range of real family crests and find out what the different symbols mean. Find out about the kind of people who would wear their family crest as a matter of course – what kind of people were they, and what purpose did the family crest serve? The children could imagine what it might be like to be one of those people, and write stories about them.

**Publicise your cause** Display the posters in the class and let the children make short presentations about their causes. Give them time to prepare something to say (children who find they are speaking about the same cause could work together). If they can find any visual aids they could bring those in, too. Limit the speaking time to five or ten minutes.

_____and

*child*

_____

*helper(s)*

_____

did this activity together

# Magic time TV

You have been given a special magic time TV. When you change the channels, it will show you a picture of yourself in the future or the past.

● You turn to channel at '+10', which means ten years in the future. What are you doing on the screen?

● Write down some more things you think you will be doing in ten years' time.

● What will your clothes look like?

● Where will you be living?

● What will your helper look like?

● Draw a picture showing what you think you will look like.

# The story pyramid

● Think about the last book you read.

● *See if you can answer these questions.*
*Write down your answers.*

1. What was the main character's first name? (1 word)

2. What was he or she like? (2 words)

3. Where did he or she live? (3 words)

4. What did he or she want to happen? (4 words)

5. What problem did he or she face? (5 words)

6. How did the story end? (6 words)

7. What happened in the best part of the story? (7 words)

8. Why would you/would you not tell a friend to read this book? (8 words)

**To the helper:**

● Do this together .
● Talk about the book before writing anything.
● You may need to help to keep the numbers of words limited to those given in the instructions.

**This activity asks detailed questions about your child's reading book and his or her opinion of it. Having to limit the words they use to answer the questions makes children think very carefully about which words to use. Back in the classroom we will share our story pyramids and so give a succinct reivew of each book.**

_____and
*child*

_____
*helper(s)*

_____
did this activity together

_____and

*child*

_____

*helper(s)*

_____

did this activity together

# Genres

● What **kind of book** are you reading at the moment?
Is it a thriller, a crime novel, an adventure, a mystery, a romance, a biograpy?
Or is it an information book?

● Write the titles of five books that you think are in the same genre (category) as your book below.

● Write a brief description of that genre.
For example, 'I think my book is a thriller because...'

● What is your helper's favourite genre of reading material?

# Cola design

● Imagine that you have invented a new cola drink for a soft drinks company. Think of a name for your product, and then:

– design a logo, and draw it in the box below.

– write an advertising slogan below.

● Write a paragraph of advertising information with your helper on some paper. Remember, you are trying to get people to buy the new cola.

**To the helper:**

● Talk about all the colas you know of already. Do they really taste any different from one another?

**This activity will make children aware of how designers and advertisers try to attract them to their products, and give them practice in writing in a similarly persuasive style. The advert could be funny or intriguing, or it could link the product to a particular lifestyle.**

_____and

*child*

_____

*helper(s)*

_____

did this activity together

_____and

*child*

_____

*helper(s)*

_____

did this activity together

# Oh, No!

● Have you ever done something that you regretted?

Perhaps something got broken, or someone got hurt, or something had to be cancelled or postponed because of you.

● Draw a cartoon strip showing what happened.
Perhaps your helper could draw, and you could do the writing.

# Future world

● Make a list of all the jobs which you think will no longer exist in the year 2050.

Librarians
Telephone operators
Bank cashiers

_____ and

*child*

_____

*helper(s)*

_____

did this activity together

_____and

*child*

_____

*helper(s)*

_____

did this activity together

# Job names

Sometimes the name of a job changes, although the job stays the same.

For example, a refuse collector used to be called a dustman.

● Think of some more jobs.

● What will these jobs be called in 50 years' time.

● Write down your ideas below.

# Computer characters

● Have you ever played a **computer game**?

● Describe one of the games you have played, including all the characters and their special powers, to your helper.

Computer game designers have to think up all these characters (although they sometimes borrow characters and settings from feature films or animations).

● Imagine that you have to invent a computer game with at least three characters in it, and a setting.

● Draw a picture of each character, and write down his or her special powers. Draw or write a description of the setting, or each 'page' of the computer game.

_____and

*child*

_____

*helper(s)*

_____

did this activity together

_____and

*child*

_____

*helper(s)*

_____

did this activity together

# One day my Mum...

'One day my Mum shouted at me for something I didn't do...'

● Write a dialogue between this child and his or her mother in the space provided. You may remember a similar conversation that you have had, or you could make one up.

# Think bubbles

● Do you always say what you think?

● Draw a cartoon of a conversation where what is said is not what is being thought.

_____and

*child*

_____

*helper(s)*

_____

did this activity together

_____and

*child*

_____

*helper(s)*

_____

did this activity together

# I am what I wear

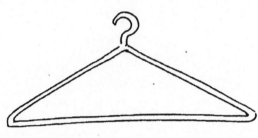

● Draw a picture of yourself below wearing these clothes and write about why they are special to you, and how they make you feel.

● Ask your helper to write down what he or she thinks about your favourite clothes!

● What are your favourite clothes?

# Parents on trial

- Make a list of things your parents won't let you do.

- Which restrictions do you think are unfair.

- Which restrictions do you think are necessary.

**To the helper:**

- Talk about why rules are important; what might happen if you had no rules in your house?

**This activity helps children to organise their writing by making preliminary lists. Back at school we shall use these skills as the basis for writing about new improved domestic scenarios!**

_____and

*child*

_____

*helper(s)*

_____

did this activity together

_____and

*child*

_____

*helper(s)*

_____

did this activity together

# Designer labels

● Why do some people think it's important to have designer labels on their sportswear?

Size 10

● What do these labels say about the person wearing them?

● Write below what you think.

*impact* WRITING HOMEWORK

# Pass it on

- Write below a review of a book which you have read recently.

- Pass it on to a friend!

Title: _____

Author: _____

_____and

*child*

_____

*helper(s)*

_____

did this activity together

**To the helper:**

● Talk about the kind of obituary your child would like. Would he or she like to be remembered for his or her actions or his or her personality? Would the obituary be serious or humorous?
● Talk about the style in which obituaries are usually written.

**By having to write their own obituaries children are having to write in a particular style.**

_____and

*child*

_____

*helper(s)*

did this activity together

# Remember me!

When someone famous dies, you may see his or her obituary in a newspaper. An obituary tells us what the person was like and what his or her achievements were.

● Write down in the space provided what you would like to have in your obituary.

## Home News

## Obituaries

# A theme ball

● Plan a theme for a grand ball. For example, it could be a space ball where everyone wears a spacesuit or comes dressed as an alien.

● Think about what the decorations should be like.

● Draw a picture and write a description.

_____and

*child*

_____

*helper(s)*

_____

did this activity together

_____and

*child*

_____

*helper(s)*

_____

did this activity together

# Yuck!

● Think of a book character who has rather revolting eating habits...

● What food combinations might he or she choose?

What about fish-head soup with chocolate profiteroles?

*impact* WRITING HOMEWORK

# My ideal bedroom

● Describe your ideal bedroom.

● What would you have in it?
Which kind of bed would you have?
A futon, a bunk bed, a double bed?

● What colour would the walls be?
What decorations would you have?

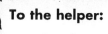

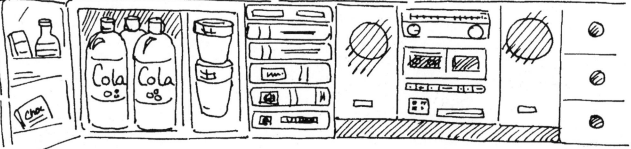

**To the helper:**

● Look at furniture catalogues and women's magazines to get ideas for this.

**Planning a setting in such detail will help children to construct convincing settings in their imaginative writing.**

_____and

*child*

_____

*helper(s)*

_____

did this activity together

_____and

*child*

_____

*helper(s)*

_____

did this activity together

# Cocktail!

● Design a **cocktail**; it must be non-alcoholic, but it can contain any non-alcoholic drinks you like!

● Write down the name of your drink opposite, and instructions on how to make it. (Include the quantities of each ingredient.)

● Write down five words that you think would describe the taste well.

# Invent a pudding

● Design a delicious new dessert.

● Write down the name of your dessert opposite, and instructions on how to make it. (Include the quantity of each ingredient.)

● Write down five words that you think would describe the taste well.

_____and

*child*

_____

*helper(s)*

_____

did this activity together

_____and

*child*

_____

*helper(s)*

_____

did this activity together

# Wake-up Saturday TV

● Design a new Saturday morning television programme for children. It should include at least two presenters, a couple of comedians, maybe a couple of puppet characters, games, interviews, music and regular cartoon slots.

● Write down on a piece of paper the name of the programme, the names of the personalities, how long it will be on air for, and a brief outline of what will happen.

# What if ... children had the vote?

- Imagine that children had the vote; how would things be different?

- Do you think there would be a children's parliament?

- Discuss this with your helper.

**To the helper:**
- Talk about what it means to vote; what are you doing when you put a cross in the box?
- What do you think about this issue? Explain what you think to your child; what are his or her views?
- What would be the new issues raised by child voters, if any?

**Being able to express a point of view is an important skill in writing. This activity gives children the opportunity to write persuasively and to justify their opinions. We shall be discussing some of the issues back in the classroom.**

_____and

*child*

_____

*helper(s)*

_____

did this activity together

_____and

*child*

_____

*helper(s)*

_____

did this activity together

# What if ... only women had the vote?

● Imagine that **only women could vote**.

● How do you think things would be different?

● Talk about this with your helper – if she is a woman, try talking to a man about it as well!

● Do you think that only women should be able to vote? Why? Write your ideas down.

# What if ... eating meat were illegal?

● Imagine that the Government made eating **meat illegal** because it was more economically and ecologically sound to be a vegetarian than a meat-eater.

● How would life be different? Would some people still eat meat, illegally?

● Do you think eating meat should be banned? Why? Write your ideas down.

_____and

*child*

_____

*helper(s)*

_____

did this activity together

# Family crest

● Imagine that you live in medieval times. Important families have coats of arms, or crests, which feature things which are important to the family.

● Design a family crest in the space.

● What might it have on it?

● Think of things to do with your family history, for example, you might want to draw a symbol representing your grandfather's birthplace, or a combination of symbols representing all the different activities your family has been involved in.

● Write what the symbols mean underneath your crest.

# Publicise your cause

● Design a **poster** that will help to publicise a cause you feel strongly about, for example, recycling, banning the testing of cosmetics on animals or banning whaling.

● Research some information about your cause and include it in your poster – people need to know why it is a just cause!

_____and

*child*

_____

*helper(s)*

_____

did this activity together

## Management

Most teachers send the shared writing task as a photocopied sheet included in the children's **Reading Folder** or in their IMPACT **Maths folder**. Remind the children that they may use the back of the IMPACT sheet to write on. Before the activity is sent home, it is crucial that the teacher prepares the children for the task. This may involve reading a story, going over some ideas or having a group or class discussion. Some ideas are provided here in the Teachers' Notes for each activity. The importance of this preparation cannot be overstressed.

Many of the tasks done at home lend themselves naturally to a display or enable the teacher to make a class-book. A shared writing display board in the entrance hall of the school gives parents an important sense that their work at home is appreciated and valued.

The shared writing activity sheets can be stuck into an exercise book kept specifically for this purpose. Any follow-up work that the children do in school can also be put into this book. As the books go back and forth with the activity sheets this enables parents to see how the work at home has linked to work in class.

## Non-IMPACTers

We know that parental support is a key factor in children's education and children who cannot find anyone with whom to share the writing task may be losing out. Try these strategies:
• Encourage, cajole and reward the children who bring back their shared writing. If a child – and parent/carer – does the task haphazardly, praise the child whenever the task is completed, rather than criticise if it does not.
• If possible, invite a couple of parents in to share the activities with the children. This involves parents in the life of the school as well as making sure that some children don't lose out.
• Some schools set up 'writing partners' between children in two different classes pairing a child from Y6 with a child in Y1 for shared writing activities, perhaps weekly or fortnightly.

None of these strategies is perfect, but many parents will help when they can and with encouragement, will join in over the longer term.

## Useful information and addresses

The IMPACT shared maths scheme is running successfully in thousands of schools in the UK and abroad. The shared writing works in the same way, and obviously complements the maths very well. Both fit in with the shared reading initiatives (PACT or CAPER) which most schools in the country also run. The OFSTED Inspection Schedules require and take account of schools working with parents as well as focusing on the quality of teaching and learning. IMPACT continues to receive positive mentions in inspectors' reports.

Further information about the IMPACT Project and IMPACT inservice training for schools or parents' groups can be obtained from: The IMPACT Project, School of Teaching Studies, University of North London, 166–220 Holloway Road, London N7 8DB.

The Shared Maths Homework books can be obtained from Scholastic Ltd, Westfield Road, Southam, Warwickshire CV33 0JH

For IMPACT Diaries contact: IMPACT Supplies, PO Box 126, Witney, Oxfordshire OX8 5YL. Tel: 01993 774408.

## IMPACT: Imaginative Writing: Key Stage Two/ Scottish Levels C-E

The activities in this book support the following requirements for writing in the UK national curricula for English.

**National Curriculum: English**
1. Range – a,b,c
2. Key Skills – a,b, e
3. Standard English and Language Study – a,b,c

**Scottish 5-14 Guidelines: English Language**

| Strand | Level |
| --- | --- |
| Functional writing | C/D/E |
| Personal writing | C/D/E |
| Imaginative writing | C/D/E |
| Knowledge about language | C/D/E |

**Northern Ireland Curriculum: English**

Purposes – to express thoughts, feelings, imaginings, describe, narrate, persuade. Contexts – first hand experiences, responses to reading, various areas of study. Range – variety of forms including personal writing, stories, diaries, descriptions, poems, comic strips, rhymes.